Queen of

Beezy Marsh is a top ten *Sunday Times* bestselling author, who has also held the coveted No. 1 slot in Canada for three months. Her work has also been published by the prestigious national Book of The Month Club in the USA and Canada. She puts family and relationships at the heart of her writing. She is an award-winning journalist who has spent more than twenty years making the headlines in newspapers including the *Daily Mail* and the *Sunday Times*. Beezy is married, with two sons, and lives in Oxfordshire with a never-ending pile of laundry.

🐦 @beezymarsh
📘 @BeezyMarshAuthor
📷 @Beezy.Marsh

www.beezy-marsh.com

Also by Beezy Marsh

Queen of Thieves
Queen of Diamonds
Keeping My Sisters' Secrets
Mad Frank and Sons
Her Father's Daughter
All My Mother's Secrets

Queen of Diamonds

Beezy Marsh

ORION

This edition first published in Great Britain in 2024 by Orion Fiction,
an imprint of The Orion Publishing Group Ltd.,
Carmelite House, 50 Victoria Embankment
London EC4Y 0DZ

A CIP catalogue record for this book
is available from the British Library.

ISBN (eBook) 978 1 3987 0777 1
ISBN (Mass Market Paperback) 978 1 3987 1889 0

The Orion Publishing Group Ltd
Carmelite House
50 Victoria Embankment
London, EC4Y 0DZ

An Hachette UK company

www.orionbooks.co.uk

*'Life tried to crush her, but only succeeded in
making a diamond'
John Mark Green*

PROLOGUE

London's Ragamuffins by Lady Dorothy Harcourt
London 1900

They beg and dance for pennies outside West End theatres, selling bunches of wilted lavender in the summer, or hot chestnuts in the colder months, in their hand-me-down clothes so tattered and torn.

But who are they, these mysterious creatures, who emerge from dark, winding alleyways and slip into the shadows when mischief is afoot? Where do they come from?

My first attempt to find out more took me to the Seven Dials in Covent Garden, accompanied by my butler, who followed me at a safe distance. I had listened intently to gossip at Mayfair dinner parties denouncing the area as a Hell's kitchen, a den of thieves, but I must confess, despite the obvious dangers, my interest was piqued.

Late one afternoon, I entered the warren of ordure-filled narrow lanes bordered by squalid tenements, in search of my subjects, rather like an intrepid explorer setting off into the jungle. Having been told to fear the inhabitants of the Dials: the thief, the boorish labourer, the wily second-hand salesman, the brawling brats and the loud, ill-dressed fallen women, my heartbeat quickened. But what I found was a way of life so *honest* in its poverty-stricken state that it was quite touching.

Yes, people are poor, but haven't we had enough of paintings of pitiful mites with sad, sunken eyes or half-starved mothers, clasping tiny scraps of humanity to their withered bosoms? I saw beauty among the detritus, like flowers blossoming in a fertile soil, which had yet to be tilled by decent society. I knew then I had to capture it all on canvas. My husband, Lord Wilberforce Harcourt, whose work you will almost certainly know from his exhibitions at the Royal Academy, has been kind enough to indulge my little hobby and provided me with the paints, easel, pencils and paper needed to carry out my research.

What, I wondered, as I perused the bustling street scene unfolding before me, of the other side of life? Of *happy* poverty! The roister-doister boys careering down the lane on their home-made carts, the girls skipping happily through the streets in torn pinafores and the merry mothers bouncing ruddy-cheeked babies on ample hips as they gossip together. I spied some women snatching a few moments to attend to their piecework, peering through the cracked windowpanes of their tenement sculleries as their little ones ran amok. The children were not wretched or miserable. They were enjoying playing in the mud! *That* is the London I believe people want to see. And so, dear reader, that is why I set about creating my first compilation, which I share with you now in this book, very modestly, for I am no great artist.

But, I humbly venture, I believe I have captured something of the spirit of the London of our day, the other side of life, that of the ordinary folk. And I would entreat you to entertain my folly a little longer, as I share the secrets of how I, a mere baronet's daughter, captured them at work and play, *my ragamuffins.*

2

Firstly, you must watch, study them in their natural habitat. Keeping your footman or butler at a discreet but reassuring distance can provide the necessary feeling of security you may need to take that first step into a neighbourhood more familiar to those below stairs. Over time, they will come to accept your presence. And a good supply of ha'pennies in your pocket can go a long way to securing that first, crucial contact with the underclass!

A favourite spot of mine is near the fountain in Endell Street, a mere stone's throw from the workhouse. I have spent many hours observing them there: young children playing in the dirt or struggling to reach the cooling waters of the fountain to quench their thirst, mothers weighed down with baskets from the slum laundry, husbands frittering their wages on penny bets on street corners and young girls, with faces so fresh and full of hope, that they are almost exquisite in their rags. I defy you not to feel captivated by them, as I was.

After many of those tentative forays, I would return, as evening fell, to the safety of my mansion in Mayfair. I sat in my studio with a good oil lamp, my pencils and my sketch book and revisited the whole scene in my mind's eye. But something was missing, and I felt the first stab of disappointment that my artistic venture may have come to naught. Then, as slumber enveloped me that night, I realised that if I were to truly recreate them, to capture their essence, I needed living, breathing specimens, just as the botanist culls the plants from the jungle floor to study them more closely. Oh, I was filled with such energy the following morning, I was unstoppable.

My servants were dispatched at first light in search of the large hamper of rags I required to help dress my specimens in my studio, by frequenting the market at Petticoat Lane.

The bundles were thoroughly fumigated, rendering them perfectly safe from fleas. Then, I, most daringly, had to venture once more into the Seven Dials to see who could be persuaded to sit for me and to recreate the vibrant scenes from my imagination.

As a brief warning to every budding artist, there may be many false dawns, no matter how many ha'pennies, pennies and even shillings you may part with to buy their goodwill. For the pledge by some wastrel to bring his chum who never washes, or the girl with matted ringlets, or the little boy with gaping holes in his boots, may lead to much frustration and disappointment.

Then, almost out of nowhere, she appears, a mischievous grin lighting up her freckled, heart-shaped face, with knotted raven tresses falling to her slender shoulders and just a glimpse of lily-white skin visible through a rip in her pinafore which is festooned with patches. Not for her, the constraints of bodices, ribbons and bows. And her feet! Her pretty little bare feet, stained with mud because her shoes no longer fit, and her mother has spent the house-keeping on gin.

She is older than she first appears, because she's never known a full plate, or a full belly, giving her an almost luminous beauty, a waif-like quality. She is on the brink of womanhood but retains the innocence of childhood.

'Wotcha, Missus!'

She is perfect. You have your model, your muse, and your work can begin!

CHAPTER 1

MARY

Seven Dials, London June 1898

The first time I clapped eyes on her, all dolled up in her finery in the Seven Dials, I thought she was one of those women who pretend to look for servants in the slums but who are really hunting for girls, to get them into trouble. They promise them a good job, with board and lodging and pay, whisking them off to houses in the country or abroad. But when they get there, the girls discover they are entertainment for some wealthy bloke and his friends to ruin with their wicked misdeeds, just for fun.

Oh, I won't spare your blushes about that kind of funny business because it's the God's honest truth, and my ma told my eldest sister who told my middle sister who told me. The chimney sweep's boy said it'd happened to his stepsister's half-cousin, or maybe it was his full cousin, a couple of years back and she was never heard of ever again, the poor cow. And that was just because she got ideas above her station and left the Seven Dials and went off to work with one of the hoity-toity families down in Surrey instead of staying home to help her dear old ma, so the story goes. Well, it ain't really a story, like I say, it's gospel and I, for one, believe it.

Posh folks simply don't mix with the likes of us.

So, when I was at the fountain in Endell Street, keeping an eye on my baby brother Jem, while my ma was taking the weight off her feet down the boozer, my heart skipped a beat as this well-to-do lady wafted by. I thought she was up to no good, with her fancy gown and her butler following along a few paces behind her. When she doubled back and started heading in my direction, well, I almost died of fright.

Her face was covered by a gauzy veil and her hat was the loveliest thing, with cream and pink flowers all over the brim and she smiled at me, like an angel, and offered me a coin in her gloved hand. It was a shiny one an'all. Silver.

I wasn't about to be asked twice. It was a florin, two shillings, a king's bleeding ransom, if you please.

I curtseyed as I accepted it because she was a toff and I thought she'd like that: 'Thank you, Missus.'

And then I stuck it in my pocket in case she changed her mind and asked for it back.

She lifted her veil and I saw her eyes, which reminded me of the violets up in Covent Garden. They were framed by the darkest lashes, and her hair was curled in a fashionable high fringe. She didn't look dangerous. In fact, she looked at me with kindness and that didn't happen very often round our way, I can tell you.

'Such lovely manners!' she chuckled. 'There's another coin for you if you'll show me around. What do you think of that?'

I shrugged and stared at my feet, which were bare and turning black as soot from the filth littering the streets. Now, I didn't mind going barefoot because it was summer, and my boots had been pawned so that Ma could have her tot of gin. She worked in the laundry, and it was hot as holy hell in there and she wasn't born to just slave her fingers to the bone for no reward. That's what she told me as she yanked the boots off my feet and dashed off to the pawnbroker to put them in hock. But I was in no mood for long walks, and I had the baby to think about. He was quite happy grubbing about in the dirt, looking for something to play with. I'd have to bring him with me if I gave her a look around the Dials.

'I'm sorry, Missus' I said, sheepishly, sweeping some hair from my face, 'I can't leave my brother, see?'

'Oh, how terribly *sweet* you are,' she said. 'Well, in that case, might I persuade you to come and visit me at my studio in Mayfair tomorrow?'

Blimey, maybe she was one of those child snatchers I'd been warned about!

I shook my head.

Some of the other girls near the fountain had stopped their game of skipping ropes and were making a beeline for us. It wasn't every day of the week you got a toff in the Seven Dials.

'Don't be afraid,' she soothed, 'I'm an artist.' She flicked open her pocketbook and showed me a couple of sketches she'd drawn of boys and girls from around the Dials, leaning on lampposts, playing in the gutter, dressed in pinafores and breeches that were every bit as tattered and torn as my own.

I wasn't sure what to say because they looked very much like the sights I saw every day and I didn't think they were anything special. In fact, it was a bit strange for a wealthy person to want to lower themselves by drawing a bunch of urchins like us. But I wanted to butter her up, in the hope she might give me another shilling. Or at least a ha'penny or two.

'Very nice,' I said politely, ignoring the poke in the ribs I was getting from the other girls, who were jumping up and down by my side, like a bunch of stupid rabbits, led by gap-toothed Polly.

'Got any more coins, Missus? Have you?' they chorused.

She beamed at them and murmured: 'How charming!'

'We're nicer than Mary!' they said, pulling at my hair. I swatted them away like annoying flies.

They were starting to crowd around my lady a bit too much for my liking.

''Ere!' I said, putting my arm out protectively to shield her, 'Shove off, you lot! She's talking to *me*.'

Her butler made to step forward to give them a clip around the ear, but she shooed him back.

'That's fine, Jenkins, no need. They are just a little enthusiastic.'

She really had no idea. They could all be proper little bitches when they felt like it, biting and scratching anything in their path. But I stood a full head taller than any of them and was noted for my left hook, which I'd learned from my da, who'd been a boxer before he joined the Merchant Navy and naffed off abroad. So I wasn't scared of giving them a clump or two.

'Well,' she said, fixing me with those beautiful violet eyes once more, 'might you come and visit me? I'd love you to sit for me.'

'Sit for you?'

'I'd like to draw you, to paint you . . . My name is Lady Dorothy Harcourt. I will pay you well for your time.'

I'd never met an artist before, let alone a lady. I thought the hoity-toity folk just sat around all day in their posh houses eating cucumber sandwiches and drinking tea.

'But, I ain't got anything pretty to wear . . .'

She laughed at that.

'You are perfect just as you are, I don't want you to change a thing. In fact, you must absolutely promise not to! No scrubbing yourself clean in the scullery or putting on your Sunday best. Do you understand?'

I didn't have any Sunday best that I knew of. Religion wasn't big in our house unless the Salvation Army were giving out free cakes, in which case I had been known to march up and down and sing along with the band, just for the hell of it. I'd even been known to sit through an entire sermon for a Chelsea bun.

'Where's your mother?'

I didn't want to tell her the truth, that she was drinking gin in the pub down the road.

'In the laundry, Missus. She's a washerwoman. She won't mind.'

'Well, you can bring the baby too, if that helps. Your mother is expecting you to care for him while she is out at work, isn't she?'

I nodded. Ma wouldn't care where I was, or the baby for that matter, as long as she had a nice half bottle of booze at the end of the day to drown her sorrows. Maybe this way, I could get my boots back from the pawnbroker and still have money left over to keep her happy and in drink, because that way, life was easier.

Ma really wanted me to go to work as a laundry maid with my sisters, earning a pittance for getting an earbashing from Mrs Dean, who ran the place and ruled with a rod of iron. Her girls worked eight 'til eight, learning to sew neat letters and numbers with red thread on a white hand-kerchief to mark the customers' clothes. I'd already proved my mettle at that, completing the work more quickly than all the rest, so she'd given me a pile of torn sheets to mend, and I did those too. Sewing was easy, child's play. I'd always had nimble fingers.

But I wanted more than a life full of endless hours toiling in the laundry, either sewing letters, or with my feet sloshing in the water from the vats or my head bathed in steam. I'd persuaded Ma that the baby-minder wasn't a good sort and it'd be better if I looked after Jem until he was old enough for school. We called her the Crawler, that old crone. She sat in a doorway at the end of our street, cradling little ones in her arms or under her skirts as the women went off to earn their pennies as charladies or worse.

Jem was a lovely baby, chubby-cheeked and curious, with big brown eyes, and I didn't want him ending up like one of the pasty-faced, skeletal-looking mites that the Crawler had in her care. She snaffled half the scraps and milk that the mothers left for their babes; I'd seen her do it with my own eyes. And she'd let them wander in front of a cart or fall over in a puddle rather than get up off her backside and chase after them. She was more interested in slurping at her tin mug of stone-cold tea. Jem was such a sweet little bundle; I wasn't going to let Mrs Dean get her bony hands on him.

Maybe it wasn't right to want to leave the Dials and I didn't want to end up disappearing like the chimney sweep's half-cousin, but this lady did seem nice, and she was offering me easy money.

Her butler handed me a card with an address on it, in Mayfair.

I'd spent long enough in school to be able to read the fancy lettering. It said 7 *Grosvenor Square*.

'It's a short walk from Oxford Street. Be there, one o'clock sharp. And don't be late,' he said, looking down his nose at me. I could tell he thought I belonged in the gutter and had no business up in his mistress's mansion. But she had other ideas.

I gazed at her departing back as she picked her way across the cobblestones, with her butler trailing in her wake, and felt little bubbles of excitement rising in my chest at what tomorrow afternoon would bring.

The other girls were tugging at my sleeves, begging me to tell them more about what the posh lady had said to me and trying to snatch the calling card from my grasp.

But I just smiled at them and kept my secrets to myself.

I'd had a glimpse of another life and I knew for certain I wanted to see more.

And nobody from the Seven Dials was going to stop me.

CHAPTER 2

Every day starts the bleeding same down our street, with the knocker-up rapping on the window, turfing us all out of bed in time to get to the factory.

My landlady has four of us bunking up in one room together in two beds, sleeping top to toe, and there's always a dash to the lavvy in the yard before breakfast, which is a lump of day-old bread, a smear of margarine and jam. Strawberry, raspberry, apricots . . . I'm not fussy. I hate every single variety.

I can't abide the stuff, you see, 'cos I have to spend all day bottling it. Once you've got over the initial thrill of the foreman rewarding you with a jar, after your first twelve-hour shift in the jam factory, you fairly want to tell him where to stick it from then on. The constant sickly-sweet gooey vats of boiling liquid seem to seep into your pores, through the ridiculous mop caps and white aprons we have to wear. When I was a kid, I'd have given my eye teeth for an endless supply of sugary jam, sticking my fingers in it and licking them clean. Now I'd rather carve my heart out with a spoon and eat that instead.

So, you may well ask, what on earth brought me here in the first place?

Well, that's a long story, but suffice it to say, I'm finding it hard to ply my trade over the water in the West End at the moment. I like to liberate fine things from people's pockets or, if I'm feeling daring, from the counter in some of the posh shops, like Selfridges or Gamages or Marshall and Snellgrove. Oh, don't judge me. I grew up poor, around the Seven Dials, and most of the girls there learned to hoist a few bits and pieces just to survive. I've a good work ethic. There isn't a day since I was a nipper that I haven't pinched something – or tried to. That's just the way I was raised. It was part and parcel of life for us urchins from those seven streets which lie just a stone's throw from Covent Garden flower market and the theatres where the posh folk go.

I know their habits, the toffs, 'cos I've spent all my life since I was a nipper looking up at them from the gutter, watching them. I've made a study of everything, from their shiny boots to their neatly pressed trousers, listening to the rustle of their beautiful dresses as they passed me by. Would they really miss a silk handkerchief that they'd left trailing from a pocket? It's more than likely the gent would have another gold fob watch and chain tucked safely in a drawer at home if he lost the one that he was so proudly sporting on his waistcoat, wouldn't he? You get the picture.

When you're a kid, and you're small and nifty, it's easy to dart away up an alley, to squeeze through the gaps in a fence or hide in a basket down the laundry when the boys in blue come looking. When you're a young woman like I am, you've got to be a lot more crafty or you'll end up with some cozzer holding you by the collar and the next thing you know, you're in the nick. I've already done three months in Holloway for stealing some stockings from Selfridges up on Oxford Street and let me tell you, that experience was enough to make me sure of one thing: I ain't never going back behind bars.

So, for the time being I have a respectable job, a mug's job, down at Pink's jam factory in Bermondsey. Oh, I've no intention of going straight for me entire life. For one thing, I don't think I can stick it. Thieving is like an itch I've got to scratch, but this time, I need to be extra careful.

Now, don't get me wrong. I've nothing against enterprising thieves, people ploughing their own furrow, taking what they need. But when someone starts trying to muscle in on my territory, it's bound to get my back up.

I'd been looking forward to going shopping all week, waiting for Saturday afternoon, so I could cross the river and visit Gamages, one of my favourite shops, on account of the fact it's stuffed full of goods that are easy to go walkabout, such as gloves, scarves, hankies and wallets. The assistants are always half asleep. Call it intuition, or a sixth sense, but as I was making my way around the counters, peering closely, picking up a few things to admire – just looking, mind you – I became aware of a presence, someone watching me from afar.

I spied her in the mirror when I was trying on a scarf.

There she was, watching me like a hawk through a pair of dark, beady little eyes. She wasn't what I'd call pretty but there was something striking about her, snooty almost, as if she couldn't .help but look down her perfect little nose at me. Her face was small with cheeks like two rosy apples, and it was framed by black curls which she had half tucked up under a felt hat. There was a smile playing on her lips, as if she knew my game well enough, and was trying to catch me at it! She found it funny. I'd even go so far as to say she was sneering at me, like an imp with mischief on its mind.

She wasn't a walker, one of those flat-footed matronly store detectives who stick out like a sore thumb in their tweedy jackets and well-cut skirts. She was too young for starters. No, I guessed she was someone out to take what chances they could. Oh, I wanted to wipe the stupid grin right off her face, so help me God, but I didn't want trouble. That might end up in me getting chucked out; I didn't want to draw attention to myself, not when I was trying to work out my direction in life.

My mind was racing. Had she been in Holloway with me? Had we glimpsed each other across the dining room as we ate in silence in our scratchy, brown sack-cloth uniforms, or took our daily exercise around the courtyard, glancing upwards to the sky, to freedom?

No, we hadn't. At least, not that I could recall.

I stepped away, briskly.

And blow me down if she didn't tail me up the staircase to ladieswear!

Now, I've always had a passion for ladieswear because of the tempting displays of silk stockings. They were my downfall, but they were also the lifeblood of my thieving operation. If I was quick enough, clever enough, I could stuff a few packets in my pockets without anyone noticing and get out of the shops fast enough to make a pretty penny on them down the pub. The trouble was, the last time I was at it in Selfridges up on Oxford Street, I wasn't quite fast enough, and I got collared by some horrible cozzer. And that's when I ended up inside.

It was just bad luck, I suppose. Now, part of me wanted to pinch something, to prove to myself that I still had the bottle for it, but that stupid baby-faced girl was putting me off. There she was, making a great show of rifling through some nightgowns that would have been ten sizes too big for her. She was a tiny thing, standing just over five feet tall, with a scrawny frame. If you didn't catch the knowing look in her eye, she could have passed for a schoolgirl. I'd had enough of her being a nosey parker, so I dashed off towards the stairs but instead of heading down, to the exit, I went up a floor, taking them two at a time, heading to menswear. She'd never think of following me there.

But she appeared in the doorway only moments after I'd made my way past the tailor's dummy in his evening suit. She skipped in, giving me a knowing wink.

I felt myself blushing with barely suppressed rage at her sheer blooming cheek and I started to rifle through a pile of silk handkerchiefs – lovely, easy pickings on any other occasion. I managed to get one inside my coat pocket but for some reason my fingers felt like fat, useless sausages, and I fumbled so clumsily that the old bloke who ran the men's department began to walk towards me, looking like he knew full well what I was up to.

In a split second, he'd be on me. Then I'd be done for, even with his limp slowing him down. Suddenly, I felt a bony little arm poking me in the ribs and turned to see my baby-faced tormentor grinning at me.

'Oh, there you are!' she chirped, 'Granny's downstairs waiting, and we must get home in time for her pills, or she'll have one of her funny turns.'

'Sorry, Mister!' she shouted at the assistant, pulling me away across the shop floor. 'We really must dash. It's a matter of life or death!'

He started hobbling faster and so we started running, arm-in-arm, towards the exit.

He was still calling after us, 'Miss! Miss! Come back here!', when we found ourselves scarpering down the back staircase and out into the bustling street, which was packed with Saturday shoppers.

My heart was racing as I shook myself free from her grasp. 'What the hell do you think you're playing at?' I spat.

Her eyes were dancing with glee.

'You should be thanking me,' she said, extending a hand in my direction. I didn't take it. 'Without me, you'd have been caught!'

I scoffed, 'Dunno what you're talking about.'

'Look,' she went on, 'I've seen you prowling around. I know what line of business you're in and I was wondering if we could work together, as a team. I'm Kate Felix.'

'I don't give a toss who you are,' I replied coldly. 'And I'm doing just fine on my own, thanks. Just keep away from me.' I felt inside my pocket and pulled out my razor, which I liked to keep for occasions such as these, to underline the gravity of the point I was trying to make.

'Is that supposed to be scary?' she said, breaking into a fit of giggles.

People started staring at us, which I didn't like one bit. This girl had a knack of drawing attention to herself. I tucked my razor inside my lace handkerchief and back into my pocket.

Then, I grabbed her by the lapels of her coat. They were velvet, soft, and attached to a pricey woollen jacket, which was intriguing because she spoke like me, a Cockney girl, but the cut of her clothes was very expensive.

I found myself staring into her eyes, which were inky black, and instead of being filled with fear as I'd hoped, were inquisitive, as if she was willing me to do my worst, just so she'd know what it felt like. I began to wonder if she had a screw loose.

'Listen,' I whispered, 'I don't know who you are or where you come from, but you'd better stay out of my way because I don't give second chances, and you've just used up your first.'

'I thought you might say that,' she replied, pushing her lips into a perfect pout. 'But I expect I'll see you around anyway. Think about it. We'd work well together.'

See me around!

I was still fuming about it when I started my shift on Monday morning at the jam factory. Her interference had nearly got me caught.

Life was hard enough without having some upstart trying to muscle in on my territory or team up with me, perish the thought.

There were so many other reasons she got on my nerves. I found myself making quite a list. What did she know about struggling to get by, with her perfect little angelic face? She had the kind of sweet looks that fellas go soft for. No bloke ever had a kind word to say to me and most of them round our way knew to steer clear of me if they didn't want a thick ear for their trouble. It's fair to say I don't suffer fools. When I was growing up, I had an older brother in the Seven Dials who taught me how to fight with my fists. I learned the hard way that most fellas are only after one thing in this life and I, for one, am not interested in giving it to them, thank you very much.

I'm tall for a young woman, so they say, with a face that's plainer than most, except for my green eyes, which even my old drunk of a mother admitted were very pretty, God rest her soul. My hair used to be my crowning glory, thick and wavy, but I had it all cut off in Holloway to stop the nits and now it reaches just about to my chin, which some of the jam factory girls think is daring and fashionable. To me, it's just practical when you're working all the hours that the good Lord sends. In any case, I hate the idea of having to wash my long hair in a freezing cold bucket of water in the landlady's yard in the depths of winter like the rest of them.

Lily's the worst. She'll risk catching her death of cold just for the sake of her ringlets. She puts her lovely blonde hair in rags each night because she thinks Ernie the foreman's sweet on her and is going to sweep her off her feet to a better life. We all know he's been feeling her up in the storeroom in the tea break because she lets him. But I've seen the way he looks at all the other girls and poor old Lily ain't as special as she thinks she is, even with her golden curls. But she won't take a telling and she's always been kind to me, so I suppose I shouldn't judge her too harshly.

It ain't really her fault, I suppose. That's the trouble these days for girls like her who are the marrying kind. The Great War's done for all the decent-looking blokes and all that's left are the dregs. They strut around London like kings and princes because they know they can have the pick of the ladies. It takes nothing for girls to start throwing caution and their knickers to the wind because they fear they'll end up on the shelf. Lily had her heart broken good and proper because her childhood sweetheart got shot to pieces going over the top just as the war was ending.

That's how I first met her, when I got out of Holloway. She was gazing into the River Thames, with her eyes full of tears and a snotty hankie in her hands.

'Penny for your thoughts,' I said, standing beside her on Waterloo Bridge, as the grimy waters swirled beneath us. I'd been wandering around, looking for a place to stay and an honest way of earning my living until I found my feet again. I'd grown tired of doors being slammed in my face all afternoon.

'It's nuffink,' she snivelled. 'Something's in my eye, that's all. Not that it's any of your business.' She turned away from me to try to hide the fact that she'd been crying.

Now, I don't know if you've ever got out of the nick with barely two brass farthings to rub together, but let me tell you, it puts you in a bit of a predicament. I had no idea where I was even going to lay my head, let alone where my next meal was coming from. I could tell by the way her clothes were clean and pressed and her boots were polished that she was a decent girl, who probably had a nice little job. And I needed one of those, so I was keen to strike up a conversation. But, truth be told, I didn't like seeing a young girl looking so tearful all on her own on a bridge. I'd read the stories in the papers and heard the chatter around the pubs just like every Londoner about poor cows who'd chucked themselves into those freezing, filthy depths to end it all and who'd been fished out weeks later all bloated and stinking. I didn't want that on my conscience.

'A problem shared is a problem halved, and all that,' I said brightly. 'I'm Alice, by the way. What's your name?'

That was when she started to blub, properly crying her little heart out.

'I'm Lily, thanks for asking,' she said between sobs. 'And I just don't see the point of going on without him. It's useless.'

'Now, don't talk like that,' I said, putting my arm around her, in case she got any silly ideas. 'There's always a brighter day up ahead. You have to get there, that's all.' That was just the sort of rubbish I'd heard the old lags in my prison wing coming out with from time to time, to give new girls a gee up when the reality of being banged up hit home.

But it only seemed to make Lily more upset.

'Robert was only just nineteen! We were going to get engaged when he came back on leave from France but he never made it,' she wailed, leaning on me for support. Her shoulders shook and tears rolled down her cheeks. 'He died a hero only a few days before they signed the Armistice. His mum's got his medals displayed on the mantelpiece, but she doesn't like me going round there too often because it just makes the pain worse for her. They couldn't even recover his body; it sank in a shell hole. I'll never find anyone else to love or to love me back like he did. We went to all the dances together and he ended up being swallowed by No Man's Land. It ain't fair!'

Loss was etched on her perfect, doll-like features, ageing her.

'No,' I said, 'it ain't fair. I'm sorry. The war was a terrible thing.'

She pulled a faded photograph from the inside pocket of her coat and showed it to me. Robert's handsome face stared out at me in his too-big uniform. It was such a waste of a young life.

Her voice fell to a whisper.

'I've tried to go courting with other blokes but every time I do, I feel as if I'm betraying him, and anyway, I'm getting older, I'll be an old maid before long and there's no-one I really fancy, except . . .'

I caught a glimpse of something on her face, a look of hope.

'Don't feel guilty about falling in love with someone new,' I said. 'I expect Robert would want you to make the best of it, wouldn't he?'

We began walking together, side by side, across the bridge towards the south side of London.

'Well, there is someone who shows me a lot of attention,' she said, brightening. 'He's an older bloke at work and he's clever as anything. He's practically the boss of the factory. But I expect he's got his eyes set on someone better than me.'

It wasn't long before she was telling me all about life at Pink's Jam Factory and her blossoming feelings for Ernie the foreman. He sounded like an absolute prat but choices for girls like Lily were limited, so I didn't hold it against her.

After a while, I felt confident enough to broach the subject closest to my heart.

'Do you think Ernie's looking for any more staff? I'm reliable, but the hat shop up in Hampstead, where I used to work, got sold to new owners and they turfed me out, so I need a fresh start.'

That was an understatement as well as a whopping great fib. The only hat shops I'd frequented were ones that I'd been stealing from. But I was desperate for a job, any job, just until I could get my confidence back. The soup kitchen and a park bench were my only alternatives, so the jam factory sounded quite alluring.

'Oh, I'm sure I can persuade Ernie to take you on. He's always moaning that some of the girls are right lazy cows, so if I put a word in, I bet you could start first thing in the morning!' She seemed delighted at the prospect of having an excuse to chat to Ernie and was walking with a real spring in her step.

She gave me a reassuring nudge in the ribs, and I smiled back at her.

'That's really kind, Lily. You're such a pal. No more moping about on the bridge, promise?'

She sighed, as if she knew that might be a difficult promise to keep. 'I'll try.'

We made our way through narrow, cobbled streets by the river, ignoring catcalls and whistles from drunken dockers falling out of the pubs nearby.

'Well, this is home for me,' she said as we rounded the corner into a terrace with pristine white net curtains at the windows and front steps that were almost gleaming, despite the rubbish blowing around the street. It was a place where people worked hard and were proud of appearances – the opposite of the Seven Dials where I'd grown up. I'd heard a lot of talk about these white curtain streets where the women toiled in the factories which were the larder of London; making everything from biscuits and breads to jams and pickles.

I shuffled my feet around aimlessly, clasping my little suitcase with my few belongings. Eventually, without me needing to explain further, the penny dropped that I was homeless. That's when I knew that Lily had a heart of gold.

'Come on and meet my landlady, Mrs Dally. I'm sure she'll find you a space. I'll tell her you're my cousin from up North London way,' she said with a giggle. 'But don't thank me yet,' she said raising her eyebrows to heaven, ''cos if you can survive her cooking, you can survive anything.'

I laughed along with Lily but after a spell in Holloway, whatever Waterloo had to offer, I knew it would feel like paradise by comparison.

You know when you meet someone for the first time, and you just hate their guts? Well, that's Ernie Sharp.

Lily's Prince Charming's even got a gammy hand from his time in the trenches. Oh, bloody hell, you'd think he was Lord Kitchener himself the way he goes on about his bravery and his war wound, but I reckon Ernie got himself a Blighty one, shooting off a finger so he'd get sent back from the front, the cowardly git.

He spied me the moment I hopped off the tram with the other girls from our lodgings as we made our way down

Staple Street towards Pink's Jam Factory and he started twizzling the ends of his ridiculous moustache. I'd scarcely had time to introduce myself before he was reeling off rules and regulations about tea breaks and talking.

'Nattering is not allowed,' he intoned, marching me past a row of miserable-looking girls pasting labels on an endless supply of glass jars, like a sergeant major inspecting his troops. 'And I will dock the pay of persistent offenders. Ain't that right, Mildred?'

Surely having a little chitchat to relieve the boredom of the thankless task wasn't a sin, was it? It sounded worse than Holloway!

A sallow-looking strip of a thing glanced up at him with frightened eyes. 'Yes, Mr Sharp.' The look on her face said it all, really.

I was spared the stinking pot of glue and its gloopy brush in that airless workroom but if I thought I'd got off lightly, I was wrong. The heat hit me first as we made our way across the factory floor, and it was followed swiftly by a sickly, sweet smell that caught in the back of my throat.

Boiling vats of red liquid bubbled up ahead, and girls in long white aprons balanced precariously on wooden stools, sweltering, as they stirred the jam with wooden poles. Others took turns climbing up a ladder with large metal scoops to transfer the liquid to a sort of bath on wheels.

'It goes without saying, you must treat the jam with the utmost care as it's scalding hot,' he said, waving his hand around.

'Is that how you lost your finger?' I enquired, spotting the top two-thirds of his finger were missing.

'Oh, no,' he said airily, 'I got this on the Western Front. A small sacrifice for King and Country.'

There was an awkward silence. I think he was expecting me to congratulate him or show some kind of gratitude for his missing finger, but knowing there were real heroes like Lily's sweetheart who hadn't come home made his flesh wound seem pathetic. So, I gazed blankly at him.

This brought about another bout of irritated moustache twiddling and he pointed to another gaggle of girls, who looked a bit younger than me, sitting at work benches on the other side of the room. They were using ladles to scoop the hot liquid from the metal bath and pour it into glass jars, as if their lives depended on it.

'You will start over there,' he ordered. 'I also dock pay for spillages, so be careful. We have a quota to fill, and I expect you to work fast. Lily is one of my finest workers, aren't you, sweetheart?'

She gazed up at him adoringly, with limpid blue eyes, as a flush of colour as red as jam bloomed on her cheeks. 'Thank you, Mr Sharp,' she simpered.

Bertha and Gert, the two other girls from our lodgings, exchanged knowing glances as they caught the look on Lily's face. They chortled to themselves, giving me a little wink that said they'd be teasing Lily about her soft spot for creepy Ernie on the tram ride home.

They were thick as thieves, those two, but being around them was useful because they were packers, built like brick shit-houses, and factories always had a pecking order. A few of the women on the work benches caught Bertha and Gert smiling at me, and that was enough for me to fit right in at Pink's, so I needn't have worried.

Bertha and Gert usually did most of the heavy lifting with the crates of jam because the fellas were always skiving around the back somewhere having a sly ciggie or a game of cards. Nobody ever messed with them, but back at

Mrs Dally's they had a softer side, teasing Lily to stop her getting into the doldrums about her lost soldier sweetheart and forcing her out to the pub for a drink now and again.

They were just the kind of girls I wanted on my side because I was a stranger in this part of town. When the factory whistle blew to mark the end of our shift, everyone huddled in their little friendship groups for the walk home and I was all alone for a few moments, feeling a bit lost in this new life I was beginning.

Until Lily appeared at my side, that is, brandishing a pot of Pink's strawberry jam and her chirpy voice chimed, 'Come on, Mrs Dally will be delighted at what you've got for your first day in the factory. It's jam for tea!'

Despite all her troubles, Lily was cock-a-hoop a few days later as we trudged down Staple Street to start our shift.

'Come on,' I teased. 'You look like you've found a pound! Spill the beans, what's your little secret?'

'Ernie says he might get me a promotion and move me to the inspection table,' she confided. 'But I've got to put in extra effort and up my quota.' The inspection table girls were the luckiest of the lot because they were spared the searing heat of the jam vats and the mind-numbing boredom of label pasting. They just had to check the jam levels, the seal of each jar and that the labels were glued on right. Frankly, it was money for old rope.

'Don't be daft, Lily,' I said, pulling on my apron and stuffing my hair up into a ridiculous cap. 'You work faster than all of us already. He's having you on. You're already good enough to go up to inspection if you want. Go and ask the manager.'

She shook her head. 'But it's down to Ernie, you know that. And it'll be more pay, more responsibility, so I'm pleased he's thinking of me.'

Whatever lies he'd told her, she'd swallowed them, hook, line and sinker. I hated him for the power he had over her, over all of us, with his daft rules and endless regulations.

'Has he told you to do anything else for him, in return for this new job?' I said, scooping a ladle full of hot jam and pouring it into my first jar of the day.

'Not exactly,' she said, flushing.

I raised an eyebrow.

'He's a good man, Alice,' she said hastily. 'So what if he does want to get better acquainted? He's got serious intentions, I'm sure of it.' She murmured to herself, 'I could do a lot worse than Ernie . . .'

Lily didn't bother with her lunchbreak. She kept working through, while me and the other girls traipsed off for a corned beef sarnie. When we came back, she'd filled another crate load of jars and was wheeling a bathful of the hot liquor back to the workstation.

'Steady on, Lil,' I joked. 'You'll blow a gasket!'

She mopped sweat from her brow and flashed me a smile. 'Ernie's serious about the new job, Alice. He told me so in the store cupboard when you were off having lunch.'

Then she scooped up a ladle brimming full of boiling hot jam and started hurriedly pouring it into a row of three jars lined up in front of her.

I was about to make a joke about him having serious intentions about getting her knickers off when there was a sickening crack and shards of glass flew upwards, mixed with the liquid, as the jam jars in front of Lily exploded.

It all happened so fast, there was nothing I could do to stop it. She gave a gut-wrenching shriek. The girls next to me dropped to the floor, as if a bomb had gone off. I stood there, rooted to the spot, frozen in horror for a moment, before rushing to help my friend.

Lily covered her face with her hands, dropping the ladle and spilling what was left of the scalding hot jam down her legs, screaming in agony as she did so. She collapsed on the floor, clutching her face and girls came running from all over the factory to help, with Ernie huffing and puffing along behind them, yelling, 'What the bleeding hell is going on over here!' Someone threw a bucket of cold water over her, but it was too late, the skin on Lily's face was red-raw and peeling off and she was writhing in agony, her hands clawing at her eyes. 'Help me! I can't see! I can't see!'

CHAPTER 3

ALICE

Elephant and Castle, June 1923

Lily lay in the hospital bed, as pale as a ghost, her eyes swathed in bandages and her blonde hair stained a horrible brown by the iodine they'd put on her burns to stop them getting infected.

She looked like she'd strayed into the trenches in the Great War and been caught in the crossfire. Truly, it was a terrible sight and all the other patients lined up in beds in the ward kept peering at her, as though she was some curiosity in a freak show. Her cheeks were burned, her lips were red raw and peeling and she could barely utter a sound as I rushed to her side.

'It's Alice,' I said, gently squeezing her hand to give her a bit of a gee. 'Things ain't looking too clever right now, Lil, but you'll pull through. I know it.'

'Everything's gone black,' she whispered. 'Doctors say I won't see again. I'm scared, Alice.'

Tears rolled down her face.

'Don't talk like that, Lily,' I said. 'You'll get better, I promise.'

A great sob wracked through her body, and her hands began to shake. The matron, who was busy bringing a drink of water to the patient opposite, gave me a dirty look, one that said I'd better not upset Lily anymore.

'I won't, I won't get better,' Lily cried. 'And Ernie won't want me now, will he? Not like this.'

'That's not true,' I shushed, holding up the roses I'd bought from the flower seller at the station, so she could smell their scent. 'Ernie gave me these for you as a gift and sends his best love. He just can't get away from the factory, that's all.'

I was lying through my teeth. Ernie had barely given her a second thought once the ambulance had carted her away from the factory and off to hospital. In fact, he'd been more bothered about explaining the accident to his bosses and trying to make up for lost productivity.

Something in her voice changed.

'Did he?' she said, breaking into a smile. 'They smell so beautiful, heavenly. Describe them to me, Alice.'

'Oh, there's half a dozen stems. They are roses, gorgeous ones, fit for a queen, and the petals are the deepest crimson. They are the finest that old Pearlie had on her stall. Ernie didn't spare any expense. He wanted you to have the best blooms in London.'

They were a bit wilted, those pale pink roses, fished out of the bucket at the end of the day by Pearlie, who was as mad as a hatter and couldn't always be relied upon to arrive at Covent Garden early enough to get any decent flowers and bring them back south of the River. I'd had a whip-round with the other girls to buy them. But there was no need for me to spoil the moment for Lily by telling the truth, was there? She needed something to believe in, to look forward to.

Matron appeared at my side, her shiny shoes squeaking on the linoleum floor. She glanced at her watch.

'I think the patient has had quite enough excitement for one afternoon, don't you?' she said. 'She's seriously injured and needs to rest. You may come and see her at visiting time tomorrow.'

I handed her the flowers.

'These are from her boyfriend,' I said. 'Would you be kind enough to put them in a vase beside her bed so she can smell them?'

Matron nodded.

As I was leaving, I whispered in her ear. 'And if she asks, they're crimson, not pink.'

I didn't have a brass farthing to spare on the meagre wages I was earning, but I made a point of bringing fresh flowers to Lily every day after that, to give her hope.

And it wasn't very easy to get hold of them.

Pearlie was a funny stick. When I say old, I don't mean she was an ancient crone, but her hair was grey and her face was lined and careworn as though she'd seen so much of life that it had knocked all the stuffing out of her. She'd had a flower stall outside the Elephant and Castle station for as long as anyone could recall. Everyone knew her because her old-fashioned long black skirts and button through jacket with its leg-of-mutton sleeves were covered in pearl buttons which she'd sewn into beautiful patterns: swirls, love hearts, flowers and across her back, a giant diamond. She even wore a wide-brimmed felt hat with ostrich feathers on the top, like the coster girls used to do back in the naughty nineties. Her white and brindle bull terrier, Geezer, was her constant companion and defender – he'd nip anyone's fingers if they got too close to her or gave her hassle.

On bank holidays, she'd wander up the market collecting pennies for the orphanage. On bonfire nights she'd give ha'pennies to the kids who built the best Guy Fawkes, and in the summer, she'd wave everyone off on the trains when they went hop-picking in Kent when the factories closed for their annual holiday.

She was a good enough sort, Pearlie, but she talked to herself a lot and some people said she was a devil if you crossed her, flying off the handle and raging like a madwoman. She didn't shuffle along, though, like some of the old ladies who were down on their luck. She glided, if that's the right way to describe it, with her head held high, like a swan.

I'll tell you one thing: they might say she was crackers, but she wasn't soft in the head.

I told her all about Lily and Ernie, and the terrible accident at the jam factory, in the hope that she'd spare me a few more flowers to cheer up my friend.

But she sucked in her cheeks and fixed me with a stony stare. 'I wasn't born yesterday, love. Nobody gets nuffink for free off my stall.'

I pulled a couple of nice-looking oranges and an apple from my pockets. I'd swiped them from the barrow boys up on the market, to tempt her. But she gave me such a look of contempt, her lips curling at the corners, that I put them away again.

'You expect me to take bits of fruit you've pinched for my luvverly flowers?' she said crossly. 'If I want that, I can pinch them myself, see? Go on, sling yer hook!'

Geezer woke up from his slumber at her feet, opening an eye. I swear he looked at me with menace.

'Wait,' I said, holding up my hands by way of apology. 'I didn't mean to insult you, Pearlie, honest. I just thought you might be willing to trade. You know they pay us a pittance up at Pink's and my mate's in a bad way, that's all. And her bloke don't give a toss. I'm having her on that he's giving her flowers, just to keep her spirits up.'

She thought about it for a moment.

'Not sure you're doing her any favours with that . . .'

I sighed. 'I can get you anything else you want. A nice pair of warm gloves? Maybe a scarf for the winter. Or a heap of those lovely pearl buttons you like so much.'

But my kind offer only seemed to annoy her more. 'Quite the thief! Where you from, girl?'

'The Seven Dials,' I said.

Her eyes lit up, with a strange kind of glow behind them.

'Oh, I bet you've been thieving since you could crawl!' She cackled with laughter. 'All the best hoisters come from round the Dials. It's in the blood.'

'I s'pose so,' I shrugged. 'When you've got nothing, you've got nothing to lose, have you?'

She cut me dead. 'Except your liberty?'

'Right enough,' I replied. I wasn't about to spill the beans on my prison sentence, but she had caught the gist of it without me explaining.

She gazed into the distance and picked a few petals from one of her roses.

'I used to know a girl from around that way, many moons ago now,' she said. 'Nice girl, she was. They called her Mary, if memory serves. She was tall, with lovely raven hair, and quite the character. Ambitious, that one.'

I didn't want to appear rude, but the slums were full of girls called Mary and I desperately needed to get a bunch of carnations, or something, to give to Lily. The matron was such an old witch about visiting times, she'd have locked the doors if I didn't get my skates on.

'Well, if you knew someone from the Dials, you'll know I'll keep my word when I say I will pinch whatever takes your fancy. So can I have a bunch of flowers, please?'

She began pulling a few stems from the bucket of water in front of her and wrapping them in some old newspaper.

'I don't want your hoisted goods,' she said, matter-of-factly. 'But I do have something else I want from you.'

'What's that?'

'Your time,' she replied, looking at me with such intensity it made my heart skip a beat. 'Come and spend an hour with me each day, chatting to me, keeping an old woman company. I will give you my best flowers for free. How about that?'

I reached out to shake her hand, which was rough and calloused, but as I did so, I caught a glimpse of the most enormous diamond ring, peeking out from under her woollen fingerless glove.

She could have pawned that and lived like a queen but instead she was eking out a living selling flowers on the streets and that intrigued me enough to entertain her demands for a daily chitchat.

'All right, Pearlie,' I said, grabbing the flowers, 'You've got yourself a deal.'

I barely gave her a backwards glance as I dashed off to the hospital. But there was something nagging at the back of my mind as I hurried along the cobbled alleyways to get to the hospital in time to see Lily.

It had been a good few years since I'd left the Seven Dials and I wasn't ashamed of my upbringing – far from it. We were all as poor as each other for one thing. But the way Pearlie had looked at me made me feel, for the first time in my life, like she understood that itch I had to scratch, the desire to pinch stuff, which ran through me like the printed words through a stick of rock. It wasn't like I had anything to hide but she'd seen right through me anyway.

So, I'd give her my time.

But I couldn't help wondering what I was letting myself in for.

CHAPTER 4

MARY

Mayfair, London June 1898

One of the barrow boys parted with his boots for the afternoon, for a shilling. It was costly, but I reckoned it'd be worth it because that posh lady was flush with money from what I'd seen.

I set off from Covent Garden in plenty of time, with my baby brother Jem comfortably tucked in a crate on a plank of wood with old pram wheels fixed to it. The boys down our street used it for races, but my need was greater than theirs and so I'd swiped it when no one was looking. I untied the length of old rope which the girls used to swing off the lamppost, so I could pull him along behind me, like a little prince in his carriage. He loved it, clapping his hands with glee as we wandered towards Oxford Circus.

We passed by grand shops with their windows full of the finest fashions. I found myself gazing enviously at the furs, the silks and the beautifully crisp cotton blouses on display, wondering what it would be like to touch them, or better still, try them on. I'd never had any reason to go up that way before now and a whole new world began to open before me. Suddenly my pinafore, which was more patches than anything else, began to feel very shabby and my borrowed hobnail boots felt ten sizes too big and quite ridiculous as I clomped along.

All around me, Oxford Street bustled with life as people with money came out to see what they'd like to buy. There were tempting smells from the bakeries, bolts of cloth and ribbons in the most beautiful colours in the windows of the haberdashery stores, and mannequins dressed in the latest fashions drawing crowds outside the big shops, with windows gleaming in the sunlight. Horses clip-clopped their way down the road, with smart black carriages jostling for space next to delivery carts, as newspaper sellers shouted out from street corners. This was a different kind of London, one that wasn't fed by scraps and watered-down beer. It was plump from the good things in life, and it crackled with a different energy.

I can't say I'd ever felt ashamed of the fact that I was poor, not living in the Seven Dials, but once I got up towards Mayfair, some folk looked askance at us, and I began to wish the ground would swallow me up whole. Others pretended not to see us, barging past as if we were invisible, winding me as they knocked against my ribs. A couple of gents in top hats and black tailcoats started laughing when a horrible gang of snooty schoolboys cat-called us 'Sewer rats!'.

And all that shouting made Jem blub, which got my back up. I shushed him as I scurried on, giving them a wide berth, turning off down a side street where things were a bit quieter. It took a few games of peek-a-boo to make him laugh again and when he giggled at me, it was like the sun coming out.

By the time we got to Mayfair, I was singing 'London Bridge is Falling Down' to keep him entertained and whist-ling to myself. I stopped to ask a policeman the way to Grosvenor Square, and he eyed me with suspicion until I told him I was going to the artist Lady Harcourt's house because she'd invited me. I waved her calling card under his nose. He chuckled into his moustache and pointed me in the right direction, towards a leafy garden square with tall, white houses all around it. Servants were busy bustling in and out of the mansions and I spotted a butcher's boy with his pony and trap and wicker baskets full of meat, as well as a laundry cart being unloaded with bundles of pristine sheets.

It was strange to think about it, but all our toil over in the slum laundries of Covent Garden and Soho ended up in these posh places. The street sweeper in Grosvenor Square acted as an unofficial watchman to keep away the hoi polloi and he very nearly caught hold of me and told me to hop it when he saw me struggling along in my too-big boots with Jem in tow. But I was too fast for him, bumping Jem's crate down off the pavement double quick and scarpering to the safety of the doorstep of number seven. The black and white tiles were scrubbed spotlessly clean, and I craned my neck to see that the mansion spread over three storeys. It had railings all around it too. My heart was pounding with excitement as I picked Jem out and held him on my hip while I reached up and pulled the bell.

Footsteps echoed down the hall and the butler opened the door, with a face like a wet weekend.

'You are to use the servants' entrance!' he scolded, shooing me off the front steps and down a set of side stairs to the basement. It made sense, I suppose. Why would the la-di-da folk want us cluttering up their nice hallways? I was used to basements because our two rooms in the Seven Dials were below street level. In the winter, they were freezing cold, and in the summer, they were the first to get the worst of the infestations of blowflies because of the damp.

But as I opened the door into the basement scullery, I was hit not by the fug of mould, but by the most delicious smell of freshly baked bread. My stomach growled like a hungry bear and Jem began to grizzle. He hadn't eaten since his crust of stale bread and a smear of dripping at first light. I gave him my fingers to suck, to take his mind off his empty belly.

'And who have we got here?' said a scullery maid, tickling him under the chin. Before I could stop her, she'd taken him from me and pinched a jam tart from a plate on the kitchen table, breaking off a piece for him to eat.

'This one reminds me of my baby brother back in Suffolk, he does,' she cooed.

Jem licked his lips and grabbed at the rest of the treat.

'Careful, little man,' she laughed, blowing on it. 'It's not long out of the oven.'

The cook was frantically rolling pastry in clouds of flour, her sleeves rolled up and sweat forming in beads on her brow.

She glanced over in our direction.

'One of Lady Harcourt's projects, I suppose?' she tutted. 'And don't be feeding him all of my jam tarts, Maisie! Get them out of my kitchen, go on. Shoo!'

She waved her arms around, sending clouds of flour flying.

I started to walk across the kitchen tiles, clumping as I went.

'And get those filthy boots off my clean floor!' she screeched.

I left my boots at the foot of the scullery stairs and followed Maisie as she climbed up, with Jem still in her arms. He was chattering away, in his silly baby talk, which meant he liked her, as far as I could tell. She was still

38

feeding him scraps of jam tart, and when he peered at me over her shoulder, he gurgled with delight.

We made our way along a hallway that had wallpaper on it, covered with gold flowers and beautiful swirling leaves and there were pictures of men on fine horses hanging on the wall too. Everything smelled of furniture polish and the banister was practically gleaming. There was carpet on the stairs, which was a bit of a turn up, because the only stairs I'd ever seen had bare boards and were usually thick with dirt.

'Her Ladyship's studio is upstairs on the right and she's expecting you,' said Maisie, handing Jem back to me.

She glanced down at my filthy boots and stifled a laugh: 'Oh, good Lord! The housekeeper will have your guts for garters if you leave marks on her stair runner. You'd better tread lightly, my girl!'

I was shaking with fear as I made my way up the stairs. Up ahead, the door was ajar, and I could hear a woman humming to herself. I knocked softly and stepped inside.

Lady Harcourt turned to face me, a smile spreading over her face. She was more beautiful than I remembered: tall, with skin like porcelain and her hair carefully curled and pinned so that it hung above her collar as if by magic. She was wearing a blue painter's smock, but the white lace on her sleeves showed off her delicate arms. Pinned at the collar of her blouse, she wore the most enormous diamond brooch.

'Oh, you are here at last!' she cried, waving a paint-brush in my direction, her jewelled rings sparkling in the sunlight. 'And you have brought your little brother with you. How sweet!'

Jem buried his face in my shoulder and her face fell, as if she was disappointed that he didn't smile at her.

'Sorry, Missus,' I said. 'He's a bit shy, that's all.'

She bustled towards me. 'That's fine, I have plenty of things here to keep him busy while we work,' she said tetchily.

There was a huge bay window with a blanket spread out beneath it. And there were toys there: a teddy bear, some wooden blocks and a box that looked a bit like a treasure chest. It was more than Jem had ever had to play with in the whole eighteen months of his short life. I felt tears prick my eyes at the shame of it. I'd got him a few wooden clothes pegs from one of the other mothers in the street and painted eyes and a mouth on them with a lump of coal but that was all he had, other than whatever he could find in the street.

'Oh, Missus!' I cried. 'You're a proper angel to do that for him. Look, Jem!'

'It's nothing,' she said, almost scornfully. 'This used to be my daughter's playroom.'

I carried him over to the blanket, which was woollen and soft, and sat him down. He clapped his hands with glee as I opened the box, and we peeked inside.

He grabbed it, and before I could stop him a whole pile of buttons had spilled out onto the rug.

'He can sit there, and we shall get to work,' said Lady Harcourt. 'What's your name, girl?'

'Mary,' I said.

'Well, Mary, you may call me Lady Harcourt. Missus is all very well on the streets of the Seven Dials but in Mayfair we do have certain standards.'

I couldn't tell whether she was teasing me, because she raised an eyebrow, but I felt myself blushing. She had a big canvas on an easel in front of her and there was a rickety old table with a chair and an empty tin plate and mug on it about six feet in front of that.

'Just sit down and imagine that you are at home in your tenement, and you have no food on the table. Show me how sad that would make you, how you would slump at that table in despair.'

I didn't have to imagine very hard because it was a nightly occurrence in my house. I leaned forward with one elbow on the table and my hand cradling my chin as I turned to face her. It was nice to have a bit of a rest after all that walking, to be honest.

'Yes!' she cried. 'With your eyes slightly downcast, that is perfect. Good girl.'

Jem was swishing the buttons around all over the place on the rug, and he kept shoving the teddy in his mouth. He thought it might have been food, bless him. But he was happy as a lark. I must have sat there for a good half hour, with my head growing heavy and my eyes half closing, before Her Ladyship tutted and held her hand to her forehead, as if she felt faint.

'No, something's not right,' she said. 'It just doesn't look quite realistic enough.'

I jolted myself upright and turned to face her.

Her violet eyes narrowed. 'Did you wash your face this morning, Mary?'

'No, Your Ladyship,' I said. 'I swear I never did that.' Chance would be a fine thing. There wasn't a cloth in the scullery anyway.

'I need you to make yourself dirtier, to make this whole scene more realistic, otherwise my whole project will fail.'

She rang the bell on the wall by the fireplace and after a few moments, I heard footsteps hurrying along the corridor and another lady appeared, dressed head to toe in black, with her hair parted straight down the middle and pulled back severely. She bobbed low in a curtsey. 'Yes, Your Ladyship?'

'Miss White, I require a good quantity of soot,' said Lady Harcourt, beaming, as if this was the most normal thing in the world to ask a servant for.

'It's summer, Your Ladyship, and it's been a while since the fires have been lit . . .'

'I dare say there'll be some little pockets of soot loitering at the back of the grate, won't there? Can't you ask the scullery maid to help you?' Lady Harcourt looked pained. 'I simply must have it for my art. I don't care if you have to go out into the square and chase down the chimney sweep, White, I want that soot!' She stamped her foot with fury. Jem didn't like that and started to get a bit teary.

I went to comfort him.

'Leave him!' she ordered, as he started to blub. 'You must not move from that spot, or I will lose my place and the whole picture will be ruined. I will attend to him.'

She went to him, gliding across the room with such grace that I couldn't help marvelling at it. Then she picked him up, holding him at arm's length, as if he were a strange kind of animal.

'Ooh, you are a smelly little thing, aren't you?' she laughed. He laughed with her, the little mite, because he was just grateful for the attention, and he had such a good nature, did my Jem. He was as sweet as a kitten.

'I might have to paint you, too!' she said. 'Are you enjoying playing with those buttons?'

He was clasping one in his chubby fingers, and he held it up. It was mother-of-pearl, a beautiful thing, sheeny in the light. And that was when he said his first word. 'Button.'

I knew when he first spoke it wouldn't be to say 'Ma' because she barely had anything to do with him; his care was left to me and my sisters. But I'd secretly been hoping it would be my name on his lips, his first spoken word.

But 'button' it was.

'Button, indeed!' said Lady Harcourt, plonking him back on the rug. 'Now, that's better. You keep yourself amused awhile longer.'

She turned to me, with a softer look on her face.

'I always wanted a son, but sadly it was not to be . . .' she began.

'I'm sorry, Your Ladyship,' I replied.

That seemed to annoy her. 'I wasn't asking for your comments! What would you even know about it?' She turned away to face the window but continued with her tirade. 'The poor seem to be able to breed like vermin, while good families, who could raise a child in the right way, who could expand their horizons and create decent citizens, are left mourning their losses! It just doesn't make any sense.'

There was no mistaking it, there were tears in her eyes when she turned around to face me. I wanted to say sorry again, but I wasn't sure what I had to apologise for, and somehow the words got stuck in my throat. That just made matters worse.

'What on earth are you looking at, girl?' she said crossly. 'Don't just stand there. We have work to do!' And she bustled back to her canvas, muttering to herself about how dull I was.

Just then, there was another knock on the door and the scullery maid Maisie appeared, red-faced from running, with a dustpan full of soot.

She gave a little curtsey before setting it down on the table in front of me.

'Thank you, Maisie, that will be all,' said Lady Harcourt, picking up her paintbrush again.

'Now,' she said, fixing me with an intense look, 'can you put that soot all over your face and down your pinafore, please? We can clean you up afterwards.'

I didn't want to disappoint her or make her raise her voice again in case it upset Jem. So I reached out and grabbed a handful of those smuts and rubbed them onto my cheeks and my forehead. Then, I dusted some down my front and, for good measure, patted another handful down my arms.

'You need to be a bit dirtier still,' she insisted. 'Put some on your dress. There's a good girl, Mary.'

I did as she asked, patting the soot all over my front and down my skirt.

Gawd knows, I must have looked like the wreck of the Hesperus and I'd never heard of anything so daft as deliberately making yourself dirty. But it seemed to make her happy because she started painting again, with renewed enthusiasm.

The next hour or so passed in the blink of an eye and Jem played until he was bored and then fell asleep. My legs were getting pins and needles from sitting so still and I was relieved when she finally looked up from her canvas to announce, 'That's all for today, Mary!'

I stood up, with clouds of soot flying everywhere, and looked down at my pinafore. I hadn't thought about how on earth I was going to get clean or explain the state I was in to my ma and sisters. Lady Harcourt seemed to have read my mind because she rang the bell again and the housekeeper appeared.

'Young Mary here may need a change of clothing to go home in.'

'I couldn't possibly do that, Missus, I mean, Your Ladyship,' I said. People would start asking questions if I turned up in the Seven Dials wearing new clothes.

'Don't be ridiculous, girl,' she scolded. 'I will provide you with some old things belonging to my daughter to walk through Mayfair in and you can take your rags home with you.' She was almost sneering at me when she said that. I tried not to let it bother me, but it was the same look those nasty schoolboys had had on their faces when they were so mean to me and Jem on the way here.

'Thank you, Your Ladyship,' I said, and I even managed a little curtsey which she seemed to like.

She put her hand in the pocket of her smock and pulled out some coins for me. I accepted them eagerly. There was a small fortune there: some thrupenny bits, at least three shillings and a farthing.

'I need you to come again at the same time next week, is that clear?'

'Yes, Your Ladyship,' I replied. 'I won't let you down.'

'Very well then, run along.'

And she shooed me and Jem away with a wave of her hand.

I clasped Jem in one arm and my coins in my free hand as I followed Miss White down the corridor and up the stairs into the attic, where she led me to a small room, with an iron bedstead, covered with the prettiest patchwork quilt, and a wooden dresser with a china jug and bowl on it. It would have been heaven to have that as a room of my own, even if it meant having to work for the likes of Miss White. It had a little window, which looked out on the garden square, but before I could so much as get a glimpse, she'd dragged me over to the bowl and poured some water into it. Then, she picked up a cloth and a bar of soap and gave my face a good going over, until it was almost red-raw.

Jem started grizzling so she wiped him too, for good measure, tutting to herself about how grimy we both were. Before I knew what was happening, she'd bustled off into another even tinier room, full of leather chests and old boxes, but even that smelled strongly of furniture polish. I swear to God, not one speck of dust stood a chance where she was concerned.

Jem smiled at her but that didn't thaw her out. She just kept muttering, 'Whatever next!'

Miss White heaved open one of the trunks to reveal a pile of crisp navy cotton pinafores and white muslin blouses. 'These,' she said, holding one up, 'belonged to a very special young lady called Millicent who is all grown up now. She is Lady Harcourt's daughter, and she was like a princess when she was your age. So, you'd better look after this dress, or there will be consequences.'

My words had deserted me. I had never seen such fine things.

'Well,' she said, 'get those filthy rags off. We'd better find something to fit you, hadn't we?'

I put Jem down and pulled my tattered dress over my head to reveal my liberty bodice and bloomers, which only got a wash once a month, if that. Ma used to do them for me in the laundry on sufferance, just to keep the lice at bay.

'Dear God, child,' said Miss White. 'Look at the state of you!'

She tutted to herself again as she pulled open a chest of drawers and threw a clean pair of bloomers and a cotton chemise at me. Rifling through another drawer, she pulled out some black lace-up ankle boots, which had been carefully wrapped in tissue paper.

My discarded clothes lay in a heap at my feet. She turned away as I removed my undergarments and put on what she had given me to wear.

'That's much more presentable, but your hair is a dreadful mess,' she said. She produced a comb from the pocket of her apron and started to yank her way through my matted curls, making me squeal.

That brought a slap.

'Be quiet! I am trying to make you look more like a young lady and less like a wild animal. We can't have urchins coming in and out of the house. Whatever will the neighbours say?'

Tears sprang to my eyes but when she was finished, she produced a looking glass from her pocket and what I saw astounded me.

'See? You almost look like a girl rather than some tearaway.'

I smiled at my reflection, but Miss White didn't like that one bit.

'Now, it's time for you to go back to whatever hole you crawled out of,' she said, bustling around the room, slamming the trunk lid shut.

Suddenly, she seized hold of me by the shoulders, her fingernails digging into my flesh. 'And don't think that just because Her Ladyship wants you here that the rest of us do. I know your type. She might lend you fine things, but you will never be good enough to wear them and I've got my eye on you, girl, don't forget that.'

I began to cry properly then because I felt so ashamed of myself. She hated me because I was poor, and a gutter-snipe, and I didn't belong in this fine mansion. It was true and there was nothing I could do about it.

Jem tugged at the hem of my new pinafore, and I picked him up and held him close, fighting back my tears, as Miss White barged past me. I followed her as she hurried down the stairs, across the hallway and down to the scullery, where she threw some new boots at my feet.

The cook was busy making a delicious-smelling stew and even she shot me a pitying glance, as if she knew that Miss White was a proper harridan.

'Please make sure this girl doesn't linger a moment longer than is necessary,' said Miss White, turning on her heel and disappearing up the stairs.

The cook took pity on Jem as I squeezed into the new boots and fastened the laces, tearing a hunk of bread from her new loaf for him to chew. My crate was still by the railings where I'd left it and I plonked Jem in, along with the barrow boy's hobnail boots, and my clothes, rolled in a tight bundle.

I'd already decided that I'd slip into an alleyway around Soho to change back into my tatty old dress and those horrible big boots, because I didn't want anyone in the Seven Dials to know my secret. But the way people looked at me as I strolled through Mayfair on the way back to the slums was different, simply because of how I was dressed.

Some folk obviously thought it was strange that I was pulling a baby in an old crate but most of them smiled at me, and a couple of gents even tipped their hats. That got me thinking and I tried to step lightly, like Lady Dorothy Harcourt had done in her artist's studio, gliding along.

Maybe I would always be an urchin from the poorest part of London, like that spiteful cow of a housekeeper had said.

But maybe, just maybe, with the right clothes and the right way of walking and talking, I could pass for something, or somebody, else.

CHAPTER 5

MARY

Seven Dials, July 1898

I became a regular face around Mayfair over those stiflingly hot weeks of high summer, always turning up promptly for my appointment to pose as a model for Lady Dorothy Harcourt, who practically swooned over how half-starved and miserable I looked in her paintings. Sometimes she got me to cradle Jem as he slept, wrapping him in an old woollen shawl. He was a very pretty baby, like an angel, and it wasn't surprising that she wanted to paint him too, but he did get heavy after an hour or so. It was like carrying a little sack of spuds because the maid kept feeding him treats.

The cozzer got used to the sight of me traipsing along past the mansions with Jem in the crate on wheels and even the crossing sweeper stopped trying to chase me away when I entered the garden square. A few times, I left my new clothes at home on purpose, so that snooty housekeeper had to give me another pinafore, another blouse, and another pair of shoes because Her Ladyship insisted that I had to look proper when leaving her house. It was worth putting up with the pinching and the slaps meted out by Miss White to get my hands on those threads. All the while, an idea was forming in my head. Every time she walloped me one, I became more determined to make something of my plan.

I always lingered in Oxford Street on the way home, gazing at the smart shop fronts and the well-to-do folk. The women were elegant, in gauzy white dresses trimmed with lace, with parasols to shield them from the glare of the sun, and the men wore shoes so shiny you could see your face in them. Their jewels appeared to me not as glittering gems, but as sweets and cakes, which were so tempting they almost made me drool. I wanted some of my own with a hunger that was even greater than the grumbling ache I felt whenever my belly was empty.

I started copying Lady Harcourt's accent, best I could, rounding my mouth when I spoke and moving with grace, like she did, as if I was floating through the air. Even if I say so myself, my impression of a hoity-toity toff wasn't half bad, after a few weeks of practising.

One evening, when the air was so fetid that you could hardly catch your breath, I was stepping lightly over the cobbles around the Seven Dials when that nuisance gap-toothed Polly spotted me trying out my posh-girl walk.

'What's your game, then?' she said, peering around a lamp post and almost hooting with mirth. She whistled to herself through the gap in her teeth, which was the most annoying sound in the whole of London town as far as I was concerned. 'Fancy yourself as a princess, do you?'

In an instant, I turned and pounced, seizing hold of her, giving her the fright of her life.

'And what if I am? It ain't wrong to have dreams, is it?' I dug my nails into her sinewy arms to make my point.

'No, Mary,' she said. ''Course not. No offence.' She'd always been a pathetic coward where I was concerned, right back to when we were nippers and I had kicked her in the shins for giving me lip while we were playing skipping ropes. I was a year older than her, and I'd never

50

let her forget it, because those kind of things mattered in the slums. Polly was usually to be found hanging about on the streets more than the rest of us because it wasn't safe for her to go home. Her ma suffered all kinds of ailments relating to the number of babies she'd produced over the years, and she was always laid up in a Poor Law ward of the hospital, surviving on a diet of watery soup and stale bread and the charity of the parish. Everyone said she'd find a way of being hospitalised for a splinter because that was preferable to being at home with her other half, who as well as being a chimney sweep and general gobshite, was a nasty piece of work, even when sober. He'd tie firecrackers to cats' tails, just for fun, to amuse the drunks after closing time, and so Lord only knows what he did to her and the six kids he'd fathered. Everyone heard the shouts and crying but everyone pretended not to notice because things that went on indoors were a family's own business, even if the walls were flimsy and the window panes were broken so you heard every word.

Polly, who was the eldest, suffered the worst of her dad's rages and they say her teeth were all crooked because he'd belted her one in the kisser when she'd fought back once. That didn't mean I felt sorry for her 'cos we all had a tough time in the Seven Dials, but looking at her eager little face, and knowing that she'd seen my uppity act, I began to wonder whether she might be useful to me, after all.

'The thing is, Polly,' I said, relaxing my grip and looming over her, 'I reckon I know how to look like a princess and sound like one, too. I've an idea how to get what those posh ladies have, like the ones we see parading up and down outside the theatres. I know their secrets, see?'

'How do you know, Mary?' she said, looking intrigued. She had always been a nosy cow. She squinted at me, the way she did when she was thinking. 'Is it 'cos you've been with that lady, the one who met you at the fountain?'

Oh, she was a proper big mouth and now she was dangerous because she had an inkling of what I'd been up to. If she breathed a word of it to her dad, it would be halfway around London by nightfall.

'You have to promise not to tell a living soul, or so help me God, I will climb in your bedroom window at night and stab your eyes out with a hatpin,' I spat.

She blanched at that.

I didn't own a hatpin, but she was none the wiser.

'And don't think I wouldn't, because I would, Polly McGuinness! You know I'm game enough and I'm stealthy too!'

'I promise, Mary,' she said, crossing herself.

I put my hand out and spat in my palm.

'Swear on it,' I said.

She grabbed my hand and shook it, just as we'd seen the fellas do when they made a deal on the street corner.

'I swear,' she said solemnly, meeting my gaze. She pulled away and wiped her hand down her grubby skirt. I smiled to myself as I linked arms with her and guided her up the alleyway to a boarded-up house that was home to a few old drunks when they couldn't find anywhere else to doss for the night.

'I ain't going in there for love nor money,' she said, recoiling with fear. Some of the mothers had told us it was haunted, to stop us getting killed by falling masonry, no doubt.

'Oh, don't be so daft,' I said, stepping over old Harkiss, who was snoozing in the doorway, having drowned his sorrows in too much beer. His wife had upped and left him last June and he'd been pie-eyed ever since. Word was she'd run off with one of the butchers up at Smithfield Market, who had a face like a King Edward potato. Some women would do anything for a decent cut of beef, and that was a fact. Harkiss was known for being handy with his fists indoors, but he seemed to have forgotten that, crying into his pint that his heart was broken, and he'd treated his missus like the Queen of Sheba and life weren't fair. That usually went on until he drank so much that he'd spent all his wages and then the landlord would turf him out, to the cheers of the other punters.

'He's too pickled to hurt us, Polly, and too drunk to notice we're even here,' I said, as Harkiss snored loudly and I pulled her over the threshold. 'Come on. We've got a pact. You're in my gang now.'

A cat loitered in the hallway, mewing hopefully for scraps, as roosting birds fluttered overhead, settling on the roof timbers, which were visible through a gaping hole in the ceiling. Rotten floorboards creaked underfoot as we crept into the front room, where wallpaper hung down in great strips. The windows were boarded up and in the gloom, the damp hung about our shoulders like a cloak.

'Why are we even in here, Mary?' whispered Polly. 'It's got bad spirits in it, that's what Ma told me.'

'Don't be daft,' I said, kneeling down and scrabbling beside the hearth to find my hiding place. 'Bad spirits, my arse.'

In the filth beneath my fingers, a floorboard wobbled at my touch, and I grasped the edge, pulling it firmly upwards. Three little bundles of clothing lay hidden where I had left them. I pulled one out, unrolling it onto my lap, dusting it off, beaming with pride. Then, I held up one of the dresses I'd been given at Lady Harcourt's, so that Polly could see it in the half-light.

'This, Polly, is our ticket to a different life, a better life than the one we've been living in the Seven Dials,' I said proudly. 'I ain't got it all worked out yet, but looking the part is the most important thing, I'm pretty sure of that.

'There's riches beyond your wildest dreams in those fancy shops. Like a fairy tale, only better. Dressed in these posh clothes we can get in and walk about, just like all the other folk. Then, we just have to be cunning and brave enough to take some of it for ourselves. What do you say?'

'I think you are stark raving mad, Mary Carr,' said Polly, her eyes as wide as saucers. But her fingers were reaching out to touch that dress, as if it was the most precious thing she'd ever seen in her life. I snatched it from her grasp.

'Can I really wear it?' she said, in a small voice.

'Yes, you can,' I said, rolling it up carefully. 'As long as we scrub your face and hands clean in the fountain first. And you can come with me up to the West End and we can go into the big shops and see what we can pinch. This ain't a game. This is real, Polly.'

I was no fool. I knew that Polly had been nicking bits of fruit from the barrows since she could walk, just like all of us round our way. It was a matter of survival, to take what you could. And I knew she was probably the most light-fingered of the lot in the Seven Dials – other than myself, of course.

'Won't it be dangerous? What if we get caught?' she whispered.

'We won't get caught,' I said, 'because they won't be expecting anyone to steal from them, not when they've got hordes of people dripping with cash and gold through their doors every day! Urchins like us don't normally get past the doorman, do we? We'd be sent off with a flea in our ear. But if we dress like two smart young ladies, well, things will be different, you'll see.'

I didn't know it for sure, but I had to believe it was possible because otherwise I'd be working down the laundry for the rest of my days. I'd seen a different side of life up in Mayfair and although I could never hope to be that stinking rich, I reckoned I'd have a good go at taking enough to make myself comfortable. What's more, I needed Polly by my side to help me and if we were successful, I'd need her to get more girls involved in my little scheme.

'Mary,' she said earnestly, sitting down on the creaky floorboards, 'this is the most exciting thing ever, like magic, or Christmas that the rich folk have with presents and tables groaning with food, ain't it?'

'Yes, Polly,' I replied, patting her on the knee, 'I believe it is.'

'I won't ever let you down, no matter what,' she said, spitting in her hand again and grabbing mine before I could tell her that wasn't necessary. There was a look on her face, a look that came from poverty and desperation, and I realised then, she was as keen on this plan as I was.

'Do you reckon I could earn enough to get a fresh start for Mum and me and the other kids?' She didn't mention her dad, but we both knew she was talking about escaping his clutches.

I bit my lip. Truthfully, I didn't know but I had to believe it was possible.

'I reckon you might, Polly. And what other chances to better yourself have you had lately?'

We were all at sea in the Seven Dials, we could drown here, and nobody would mourn either of us urchins, but somehow fate had thrown us a lifeline. It didn't matter that we were going to be nicking a lot more than just bits of fruit to stave off hunger. Where was justice when we were being beaten by our parents or going to bed hungry or sworn at by strangers, just for wearing ripped and dirty clothes?

Life had given me a chance, and I was prepared to grab it with both hands, whatever the risk. And now Polly was coming with me.

Whatever the future held, there was no turning back.

I woke early in the dingy back room I shared with my sisters, as the thin morning sunlight streamed through the scrap of linen Ma had hung up as a curtain. We slept top to toe, me and Ada, who was a year older than I was, fighting over the blanket half the night. Susan was the eldest at eighteen and she had her own bed that Ma had got from the rag and bone man for a good price. We'd spent ages stuffing the mattress with straw to make it less saggy, but it came with some unwanted guests – bedbugs – and now we all suffered for it. Sometimes the bites were unbearable, and no amount of vinegar could take the sting out of them.

Jem was dozing in an old drawer at the foot of my bed. We'd padded it with sheets and a blanket to make it cosy, but he'd nearly outgrown it, his arms and legs splaying over the sides. When he got a bit bigger, he'd have to get in with Susan and God knows, she'd grumble about it. I wouldn't have minded him in with me, but Ada would moan about that. She was born under a cloud, that's what Ma said about her. She was always whining about something or other.

I sighed as I put my feet down on the bare boards and pulled on my clothes, before taking the threadbare pillow-case from my pillow. Then I picked up Jem, who was still snoozing, and carried him through the one room at the front, which was a scullery and living room and which led straight out through the front door onto the street.

The church bells chimed five as I wandered over the cobbles towards Covent Garden. It was the same route I took every day, to get to the bakery and join the queue with the other kids. There was no shame in it, not the way I saw it. We queued up for handouts of day-old bread and buns for breakfast for a penny at Godden and Hanken.

Flower sellers were already at their pitches, bustling about in their long black skirts, with baskets of blooms, and the horses for the delivery carts were standing in their blinkers with a nosebag full of oats, ready for the day to begin. Costermongers bellowed their greetings to each other as they wheeled their barrows along. The racket was deafening if you weren't used to it.

As I joined the back of the queue, which was already about ten feet long, there was something in my stomach that was different to hunger. It was excitement about what the day would bring now I had my first recruit, Polly. I started daydreaming about us thieving until we could live like queens, swathed in furs and diamonds, riding in fine carriages pulled by gleaming horses.

A sharp poke in the ribs brought me back to reality.

A girl with hair like rats' tails, who was missing a front tooth, hissed at me. 'It's your turn. Go on! Hurry up!'

I stepped inside the shop, which was filled with wonderful smells of fresh bread and buns, and the baker broke into a grin at the sight of Jem in my arms. I held out my penny and he took my pillowcase, stuffing it to the gunnels with yesterday's unwanted loaves. Then he picked up a couple of iced buns from the counter and popped those in as well.

'That'll do for the little 'un, won't it, petal?'

'Thanks ever so much,' I said, with gratitude.

I swung the pillowcase bulging with bread in one hand as I tucked Jem on my hip and held him with the other, heading for home. If it weren't for the kindness of the baker, half the neighbourhood would be in the workhouse supping gruel.

The seven alleyways of the Dials lay before me, each one a pathway to struggle and despair. One day things would be different for me, I could feel it.

And that day had begun.

It only took a couple of pennies and a sharp word from Polly to persuade some of the other girls it was worth their while looking after Jem for the morning.

'And don't tell a living soul,' said Polly, yanking a few plaits for good measure. 'Or you'll be for it!' She absolutely loved her position as my new best mate and deputy and practically strutted about like a pigeon with self-importance.

We waited until all the mothers had gone off charring or to the laundry to slip into our hiding place and get changed into our new clothes and shoes, giggling at how different we looked. Then, when the other girls were playing chase, we slipped away down the alley, heading towards Oxford Street. We were so excited, we skipped along together arm-in-arm.

'When will we get to Selfridges, Mary?' said Polly, her face lighting up.

'All in good time,' I replied. 'First of all, we need to have a trial run in one of the smaller shops, just to see how we are going to work together. Clear?'

She nodded.

Although I hadn't really thought it through, I reckoned half of this game was sounding confident because I needed her to help me and not lose her bottle or we'd be sunk.

'Remember your manners and try to talk proper, like you are meeting the Queen,' I said. 'You ask to look at some things and I will see what I can swipe. If it don't work we'll have to run like the clappers. So be ready.'

We rounded the corner onto Beak Street, and a haberdashery shop loomed up ahead, its window filled with bolts of cloth in every hue, ribbons and accessories for smart ladies and gentlemen.

'Let's start in here,' I said, ignoring the butterflies in my stomach.

The shop bell chimed as we pushed open the door and a small fella in a waistcoat, with his shirtsleeves rolled up, stopped cutting lengths of navy silk on the counter. He peered at us over his half-moon spectacles, and I gave a little curtsey, nudging Polly in the ribs to make her do the same. He didn't look askance at us, or tell us to hop it, so I guessed our clothes must have fooled him right enough.

'What can I help you young ladies with today?' he asked.

Polly glanced around her and gestured to a tray of lace collars that were neatly laid out in a glass-front display cabinet in the corner.

'I'd very much like to see some of those, please,' she said sweetly.

He produced a little key from the pocket of his waistcoat and went around the counter to unlock it. The minute his back was turned I started to pull a length of the silk he'd cut across the counter. I turned, feigning interest in the window display of colourful ribbons as I rolled it and shoved it down my blouse and into my liberty bodice.

Polly coughed loudly. 'What do you think of this one? Does it suit me?'

I span around. She was holding the collar up to her neck and grinning from ear to ear.

'I'm not sure that Mother would like that one,' I replied, in my poshest voice. 'It's rather big on you. Are there any others?'

The haberdasher turned his back, rootling around in the basket, and while he did so I put my hand into the window and snatched two spotted silk handkerchiefs from the display, stuffing them down my blouse.

'What do you think of this one?' said Polly loudly. She'd gone red as a beetroot, and I was a bit worried she was going to give the game away.

'No,' I said, firmly. 'It makes you look like an old maid.'

The haberdasher raised his eyes to heaven and said something about young ladies being hard to please these days.

'Sorry to have wasted your time,' I said, putting my arm through Polly's and steering her to the doorway. 'Perhaps we'll call again another day.'

He locked the cabinet, shrugged his shoulders and returned to his bolt of silk.

We darted out of the shop and scurried along Beak Street before he had time to realise some of his stock had gone walkabout. I was breathless by the time we reached Regent Street, and Polly was talking ten to the dozen about what we'd managed to achieve already. It was a good start but there was no way we could just stuff things down our tops all day long. I felt the coins in my pocket, the ones I had been given by Lady Harcourt.

'We'll buy a carpet bag each when we get to Selfridges,' I said. 'Something to keep our shopping in. But you've got to stop blushing when we're pinching stuff, or you'll have us both arrested.'

She giggled. 'Sorry, Mary, it's just me nerves.'

We wandered along together, taking in the sights, feeling like we were part of the crowd, rather than slum girls who didn't belong. Nobody gave us funny looks and, in fact, I'd say gentlemen were kind to us, stepping off the pavement to let us pass. Hackney carriages were weaving their way past delivery carts in the road, and in the distance, the horses of the crowded omnibus were going at a trot.

Polly gazed in wonder as I pulled a silk hankie from my blouse and handed it to her.

'You talked like the Queen in that shop,' she said, wiping her nose on it. 'Can you teach me?'

''Spect so,' I said. 'You'll have to practise rounding your mouth and not dropping your aitches. Ladies always talk quietly and politely.' That weren't exactly true where the housekeeper, Miss White, was concerned because she was a wicked old trout but there was no need to bother Polly with that.

When we reached Oxford Street, we stopped for a moment in front of the fanciest building I ever did see, a music hall, which had arches and columns in gleaming white stone, and a huge golden banner emblazoned across the front: 'MATINEE PERFORMANCE, Ali Baba and the Forty Thieves'. A bloke in a top hat and red tailcoat was strutting about the entrance trying to drum up trade: 'Get your tickets 'ere! Show of the century. You'll be amazed, step right up!' An accordion player was squeezing a jaunty tune at his side to add to the gaiety of it all, as two gas jets either side of the door shot out flames. Top Hat strode towards us, his vast, bushy moustache twitching with the prospect of a sale. 'Step inside, my dears, you won't be disappointed. Enter the world of the Forty Thieves, marvel at their magnificent treasures, see costumes from the Far East . . .'

'Not today, my good man,' I said, waving him away. It did sound like it would be very entertaining because the farthest east I'd ever been was Hackney, but we hadn't the time to spare. 'I'm afraid we have urgent business up in Selfridges.' That brought another gale of laughter from Polly, who was clearly having the time of her life and found my lah-di-da accent hilarious.

'Now,' I said, with a note of steel in my voice, as we walked on, 'pull yourself together, Polly. This is a serious business we're about and I ain't getting collared by the law because you keep drawing attention to us with that silly laugh of yours. This is work. And I reckon if we can pull this off, we might be onto something good.'

'We could start our own gang!' she said, 'I've always wanted to be in one of those, like the boys do.'

She had a point – us girls never had gangs; it was always the lads running amok and putting their heads together to get up to no good. Well, maybe we could go one better and have a gang that did something other than get on the mothers' nerves and end up with thick ears being dished out all over the Seven Dials.

'We'd do better if there were more of us in on it,' said Polly. 'Just imagine what we could nick if we had a proper team of us going round the shops.'

I pondered that for a moment. She was right, but we'd need to be sure that some of the blabbermouths around the Dials weren't going to grass us up, so it would have to be like a secret society, something they'd be scared to tell anyone about.

'We could very well do that, Polly,' I replied. 'But we need a name. All the best gangs have names. What about the Dials Devils, or the Secret Stealers?'

She pulled a face.

Then I had a bright idea. I remembered the music hall and its golden banner.

'Come to think of it, why don't we call ourselves the Forty Thieves?'

Her eyes lit up.

And in that moment, I knew I was onto a good thing.

CHAPTER 6

ALICE

Elephant and Castle, July 1923

'Ernie ain't ever coming to see me, is he?'

Lily's battered face was etched with despair as she clasped the bunch of roses I'd got from Pearlie's stall. Her eyes were still swathed with bandages and some of her wounds were sticky and weeping, no matter what the nurses did to make them heal.

'He's busy, that's all,' I lied, catching the look of disbelief on the matron's face as she marched past the foot of the bed.

'They've had a load of oranges come in and we're making marmalade,' I went on. 'You know how bad it gets when the oranges arrive, Lil. It's chaos on the factory floor and Ernie's right in the thick of it.'

There wasn't an orange in sight in Pink's factory. It had been ten days since the accident and the miserable swine hadn't been to see her once, not once, despite me reminding him. The last time I had practically begged him when I collared him as he was rushing off down the boozer at the end of his shift.

But he'd just looked at me as if I was barking mad and found an excuse to leave, sharpish, batting me away like an annoying fly.

Lily winced in pain as big salty tears started to roll down her cheeks. 'I don't blame him, Alice. I must look like a monster.'

'No, Lily,' I said. 'You're still beautiful, and you will get better in time. You're just sick right now in the hospital, that's all.'

She lowered her voice to a whisper. 'I let him touch me, Alice. I let him. More than once. Because he promised he'd make an honest woman of me, and we'd have a big party down the pub for all the factory on our wedding day. And, he would have done too, if I hadn't made that stupid mistake. It's all my fault.'

'Oh, Lily,' I said, reaching out to hold her hand, a knot of anger tightening in my stomach. 'Don't upset yourself about it now. It wasn't your fault. He took advantage of you.' She lay there, almost lifeless.

'And as for the accident, the glass broke, and it could have happened to any of us. It ain't your fault,' I said.

The fact was, she had been rushing because of that sod Ernie and his bloody quotas but there was no point saying that now. We sat in silence, listening to the murmur of visitors chatting to other patients. Then, out of nowhere, she said the words which chilled me to the bone: 'I'd be better off dead, Alice.'

As I wandered out of the hospital after visiting time, I felt something bubbling up inside my chest at the injustice of it all; a feeling of anger so explosive that if I'd been made of glass, I'd have splintered into shards myself.

It was a hot Saturday afternoon and the trams and buses sent clouds of dust flying up all over the place as I wandered across Waterloo Bridge and up the side streets into the West End. The whole place thrummed with energy, and I was drawn to it, like a bee to honey.

Maybe I wanted to just distract myself from how I was feeling, or maybe it was a genuine itch I had to scratch, but there was no point fighting it; I had the urge to go shopping and see what I could pinch.

I was just stepping out to cross the road, to go into Selfridges, when a huge shiny black car screeched to a halt right in front of me, almost knocking me flat. A bloke popped his head above the windshield. 'I say! Are you all right?'

I think he meant it as an apology, but the woman sitting next to him, who was wearing a cloche hat, with strings of pearls at her throat, seemed to think it was all my fault.

'Don't apologise to her!' she shrieked. 'She wasn't looking where she was going, the silly little fool.' She had a long, thin face and a pointy nose and she looked down it at me. I stood there for a few seconds, like an idiot.

'Well,' she said, her eyes narrowing to slits, 'what are you staring at? Haven't you got a job to go to?' She threw her head back and laughed as her husband shrugged his shoulders at me before climbing out and opening the door for her. I caught sight of the folds of her drop-waisted silk dress and her dainty shoes as she stepped out, brushing past me as if I didn't exist.

Suddenly my thin, drab cotton overcoat, faded skirt and worn leather boots felt very shabby. Nobody gave a damn about factory girls like me and Lily. We toiled long hours in pointless jobs and for what?

Now, as I followed that snooty cow through the revolving doors and into Selfridges, where the most beautiful fashions were on display, I felt a renewed sense of determination to get away with something nice. Stealing had always been a part of my world, something of a necessity to get food as a nipper in fact. And then, as I grew older, it was just a bit of a game, a way of earning a few extra pennies and sticking two fingers up to posh people.

But the way they'd looked at me, like I was worthless, ignited something in me. I'd never be a proper toff like that snooty cow and her stupid husband, but at least if I could hoist something good, I could have some of the luxury they took for granted.

I loved crowds and the sea of people swarming through Selfridges did not disappoint. I positioned myself in the thick of it all, squeezing next to a couple of old dears rifling through rails of blouses.

I was hot with excitement but also anger at that stupid rich woman and how small she'd made me feel and my fingers were almost burning with anticipation. Two women beside me were chatting to each other about the pretty pink roses on the blouse they were holding up to admire. I opened my coat and quietly pulled another blouse from its hanger, shoving it inside the waistband of my skirt. Then, I closed my coat and sauntered off to the changing rooms carrying a couple more tops under my arm.

The assistant had the harassed look of a woman who just wanted it to be closing time. She mopped a bead of sweat from her brow as she waved me to a changing cubicle in the corner, which was covered by a thick curtain. I stepped inside.

Quick as a flash, I pulled off my coat and unbuttoned my blouse, yanking the stolen one from under my skirt. I slipped it on, glancing at myself in the mirror. It felt cool and crisp against my skin and as I did it up, I had to admit, I didn't look half bad in it, which was very pleasing. I put my old blouse on over the top. The collar was frayed. I'd chuck it in the bin when I got home, now I had a nice new one.

I had a bit of a spring in my step when I plonked the other two tops back on the counter. 'They're too small,' I said, with an apologetic shrug. I practically skipped over to the lingerie department where there was a bit of a commotion in the corner, where stockings were piled on a round table, with a 'special sale' banner over the top.

Women were gathered around like a pack of hungry wolves, grabbing packets, two for the price of one. I joined in. But instead of joining the long queue snaking around the department, I shoved a couple of packets in my coat pocket.

I had a fluttering feeling in my chest: excitement and pride at what I'd achieved so far. It was as if being looked down on by that posh woman had ignited something in me, a drive and determination to take something that life hadn't handed to me on a plate.

Now I just needed to get out with my loot.

And that is when I spied her, that crafty little girl who'd followed me around Gamages a few weeks ago. There she was, sauntering along with a carpet bag slung over her bony little shoulder as if she hadn't a care in the world, but I'd bet my last farthing that she had a bag stuffed full of hoisted goods.

Well, I hadn't forgotten the fright she'd given me, not for a minute. I am one of those girls who holds grudges and keeps scores, so I decided there and then that I'd return the favour.

Although she was quite small, it was easy to follow her without being seen because she was so wrapped up in herself, pleased as Punch with her hoisting. She was wearing a lovely royal blue drop-waisted dress, very fashionable, with a wide lace collar. She'd clearly had a good day of it because she only spent another five minutes pretending to peruse some dresses before she wandered down the stairs and into the street.

The breeze lifted the hem of her skirt, revealing her shapely legs as she headed along Oxford Street, peering in a few windows. I watched her like a hawk, almost mesmerised by the way she moved, the curl of her hair against the nape of her slender neck, the gentle sway of her hips. If I could reach out and touch her skin, it would feel like silk, I was sure of it. I started to wonder if she'd cry or gasp when I grabbed her. I was so much bigger than her, stronger. Kate Felix would be no match for me. I'd plunge my fingers into her carpet bag and take what she'd stolen, seizing it for myself.

I skulked along about ten paces or so behind her. Passing a newsstand, I grabbed a copy of the evening paper, chucking the boy a penny, so that I had something to hide behind if she turned around. But she didn't. She stuck her perfect little nose in the air and hopped onto a tram, heading over towards Whitechapel. I waited a moment, letting a few passengers get on, before I did the same.

Now, don't get me wrong, I am a Londoner through and through, but I've never liked the East End, mainly because there are gangs that I was warned about when I was just a girl. It's funny how those stories stick with you, well that and the ones about Jack the Ripper, because God knows, the Seven Dials weren't exactly paradise. But you know your home turf and mine was the West End and these days, the Elephant and Castle, and that was about the sum of it. I'd never had any real desire to head east. Until now.

The tram rattled along, rocking from side to side, and I could almost feel myself nodding off in the warmth of the late afternoon, daydreaming about how I'd make Kate Felix regret the day she'd crossed me. I had to keep pinching myself to stay awake. We were nearing Petticoat Lane when she stood up, brushed the dust off her dress, and hopped off, in that sprightly way she had about her. I was the last to alight, keeping a safe distance.

The stench of the market hit me first. Hawkers on the corner were flogging off the last of their wares to the poorest housewives, who had to wait until the end of the day in the hope of getting a bargain for supper, even if it was just the scrag-end of lamb or mince that was mostly gristle. Rotten bits of fruit and old cabbage leaves lay strewn in the gutters where barrow boys had plied their trade.

It was a way of life that hadn't changed much since before the Great War, and in the years before that, right back to the days when the East End costergirls tightened their corsets and proudly plonked ostrich feathers in their hats, kicking up their skirts down the boozer in the hope of attracting a decent husband.

Before they knew it, they'd be dancing to some fella's tune, scraping a living, working their fingers to the bone, heading to the market, drowning their sorrows in the pub. East End girls were always full of sob stories; I'd heard enough to last me a lifetime. Mugs, the lot of them. But Kate Felix was different. She had something about her, and the more I watched her wandering slowly over the cobbles, the more I was intrigued by her. It was almost as if she didn't quite fit in, like a diamond that had landed in a pile of manure.

Screeches of laughter and snatches of song escaped from the open windows at the Frying Pan pub in the middle of Brick Lane. It was a bit early for a knees-up, but it was the East End, after all, so I couldn't blame them. Suddenly, the doors swung open, and a fella staggered out, coming to a halt right in front of Kate. He started to windmill his arms around, his beady eyes bloodshot behind round glasses, practically frothing with rage, as he yelled at her.

'Where the hell have you been? I've been looking for you up every sodding alleyway 'cos I know you've been hiding from me, you lazy, good-for-nothing.' Tufts of hair stuck out above his ears on either side of his balding head. He looked like a screeching owl about to devour a tiny mouse.

With that, before she even had time to open her pretty little mouth to reply, he clobbered her one, right in the jaw. She reeled backwards, legs splaying, dropping her bag, landing on her arse at his feet. He was slight, not that tall for a bloke, but he aimed a powerful kick at her, as if he was booting a vicious dog. 'How dare you defy me! After everything I've done for you! How fucking *dare* you!'

'I didn't, I didn't,' she sobbed, pulling her knees in close and covering her head with her hands as his foot connected with her stomach. 'I did all the work you told me to. I left it back in the shop under the counter.'

She started rocking back and forth. 'Please don't hit me no more!'

He stopped and thought about it for a split second, musing to himself. 'Well, I never looked there. You must've hidden it from me on purpose, you ungrateful wretch. You're sneakier than your mother ever was, and she was trouble. It was a mercy when she died. You're just a good-for-nothing and don't you forget it!'

A few people had started peering out of the pub door, watching the commotion like it was a night at the music hall. Nobody offered to help her. A barrow boy walked past, wheeling his cart, whistling to himself.

'Come back inside, Johnny,' said a big woman, who had a bright red face and hips wider than the back end of a trolleybus. 'She ain't worth the bother, the little minx.' She fixed Kate with a gimlet eye, her mouth curling with pleasure at her distress. 'You need to be more grateful for everything he's done for you – saving you from the orphanage for starters.' Johnny staggered towards this overblown harpy, blowing her a kiss, 'Thank you, my love. Mine's a pint, if anyone's asking.'

And with that, the door to the Frying Pan pub swung shut.

Kate Felix sat on the cobbles, a mass of snot and tears, the contents of her bag strewn in the dirt. She cried softly to herself, hugging her arms around her skinny little waist for comfort. The sun was going down and the sky above the rooftops was streaked with pink as I approached. I kneeled down beside her and she glanced up at me, with a look of disbelief that swiftly turned to anger that I'd seen her in this state.

'Get away from me!' she spat. 'I don't need your help and I don't want your pity neither.' She started frantically pulling her bag closer, grabbing for things that had spilled out onto the ground, wincing with pain.

I reached out and touched her on the shoulder, gently, because I didn't want to frighten her, not after she'd been beaten up by that balding twerp. I wanted to put my arms around her and hold her close, to try to make it better. But I knew in this world, for girls like us, that was never a guarantee and I've never been one for breaking my word. So, all she got was a friendly pat.

'It's all right,' I said. 'I ain't going to hurt you. And I won't bother with pity because frankly, these days, it's in short supply and none of us need it anyway, do we? Pity ain't going to pay our bills or get us where we need to go.'

She wiped her nose on the back of her hand. We gazed at each other for a moment.

'I've been thinking about your offer the other day, to work as a team,' I blurted, before I even knew what I was saying. There was something about her that was mesmerising and I couldn't explain why, but I knew I wanted to be near her, to know more about her and that would involve spending time together, which seemed like a good thing.

'I think we'd work well together. I'm in, if you still want to, that is?'

She nodded at me, as if she couldn't quite believe it herself.

I began to help her gather up the things she'd hoisted from Selfridges, stuffing them back into her carpet bag. She'd done well, better than I ever had, to be honest. There were some nice leather gloves, packets of stockings, a few silk scarves and hankies and – no word of a lie – an entire women's skirt suit, in the finest woollen cloth.

I held that up in disbelief. 'How in the name of God did you pinch this?'

She smiled at me, with that impish grin, lifting her skirt to flash the most voluminous pair of bloomers I have ever seen in my life. They reached to her knees and were elasticated.

'These,' she said, pulling herself up and dusting herself down, 'are my secret weapon. I made them myself. They're my hoister's drawers.'

I couldn't help hooting with laughter at the sight of them. We linked arms as we walked round to her place. She stopped in front of a tailor's shop, shrugging her shoulders by way of apology. 'This is where I live. It's Johnny's business. He's the boss and the one who beats me up.' Her voice fell to a whisper and I clenched my fists with barely suppressed rage at what she had to put up with.

But seeing the tailor's dummy in the window, dressed in a neat suit with a smart collar and tie, her beautifully-made clothes started to make sense. I couldn't help admiring how she'd made good use of everything that life had put her way. That was a nice quality in a thief. She produced a rusty key and unlocked the door.

'How long have you been a seamstress?' I enquired, as I followed her inside and through to the back of the shop.

'As long as I can remember,' she said. 'My mum died when I was a baby, and Johnny and his missus took me in. He had me sewing as soon as I could thread a needle, to earn my keep.' There was no point asking where her father was. She was from the East End, after all.

We climbed the stairs to a tiny attic room, which had grimy windows overlooking the street, and a few home comforts, such as a rag rug on the bare boards. She pulled a leather trunk out from under the bed and flipped the lid open. It was filled with things she'd nicked: silk blouses, a few packets of stockings, lace collars, gloves, a felt hat and there was another pair of those ridiculous bloomers.

'It looks like you are doing better than I am,' I gasped.

'Maybe I am,' she said, sitting down on the bed, which sagged almost to the floor and creaked because its springs were knackered. Her dark eyes filled with tears. 'But I can't go on like this. I've had enough of him knocking the stuffing out of me and that wife of his gloating every time he hits me.' Her shoulders began to shake, and she hid her face in her hands, her shoulders heaving with sobs. 'I don't feel like I belong here. They hate me.'

'You can get out of here,' I said, kneeling in front of her. 'Come back to the Elephant and Castle with me. You can bunk up at my place, I'll speak to the landlady, we'll work something out.'

Her face brightened. 'Do you really mean that?'

I nodded.

'But I don't even know your name!'

73

'It's Alice,' I said, standing up and extending my hand to her. We shook hands, like we were a couple of posh blokes meeting for the first time.

'How long have you been hoisting?' I said, desperate to know how she picked up her skills.

'For as long as my uncle has been clobbering me,' she said ruefully. 'I started off down Petticoat Lane, nicking a few bits off the stalls to make myself feel better. Then it became a sort of challenge to myself, to become more daring, to see what else I could pinch without being spotted. I started heading up West, to the big stores, where there were rich pickings. It made me feel good about myself. And to avoid getting caught, I thought about how to make it easier, which is why I made my hoisters drawers.'

She was a bright spark this one, I could tell. She'd thought about the game more carefully than I ever had.

'Then, when I saw you the other week up in Gamages, I knew what you were up to, and I thought I might have found someone to have some fun with,' she added.

I raised an eyebrow.

'*Our* kind of fun,' she said. 'It's a thrill when you hoist something and get away with it, ain't it?'

I smiled at her, and she grinned back. We both knew that fluttering feeling in your belly when you'd got a lovely pair of silk stockings in your pocket, and you were headed for the exit without being tumbled. And then, walking off down Oxford Street, blending in with the crowd, smiling to yourself, or maybe humming a tune, all the while wanting to punch the air and jump for joy because you'd left the shop and you had something nice to flog down the boozer.

She picked up her few belongings and chucked them in the leather trunk, slamming the lid shut.

'I've got nothing keeping me here,' she said matter-of-factly, 'so if you're serious about your offer, I'll come with you.'

'I reckon we can make a go of this hoisting lark, Kate,' I said, as she took one end of the trunk and I took the other, bumping it down the narrow staircase and into the street. Poor Lily was never going to return to the jam factory, and although it was early days for her recovery, I knew in my heart of hearts that she'd always need someone to care for her. I couldn't abandon her, she was my pal, so I was going to have to find the extra cash from somewhere. I didn't have it all worked out, but I knew one thing for certain: me and Kate Felix were going to be as thick as thieves.

CHAPTER 7

ALICE

Elephant and Castle, July 1923

'And where the bleeding hell've *you* been?'

Pearlie's face set like concrete and her eyes were like flints as she pursed her lips and muttered her disapproval. I'd spent so long over in the East End that I'd completely forgotten visiting time with Lily and missed my chat with the flower seller. And now she'd caught me red-handed lugging a leather trunk along outside the station, with Kate Felix in tow. That dog of hers started to growl in my direction, as if it would get some pleasure from taking a chunk out of my hand.

'I'm sorry, Pearlie . . .' I began.

But she cut through me, like a knife through butter. 'Don't waste your excuses on me, girl! We had a deal. You broke it. I s'pose you thought I wouldn't mind you gallivanting about because I'm just an old woman, but I *do* mind, see?'

I'd spent ages in the past week or so listening to her stories about Mary from the Seven Dials; how she'd gone up to Mayfair to pose for some toff artist and then decided to put on the posh to go stealing in the West End with some of her pals. It was all a good yarn, I suppose, but she didn't half go on. Pearlie could talk the hind leg off a donkey, and she never let me get away on time, which meant I had to run to get to the hospital. But now she was behaving like I hadn't kept my side of the bargain, even though she'd bent my ear for her stupid flowers. But I still needed her, so I chose my words carefully.

'I'll make it up to you, I promise,' I said. 'I'll spend longer with you tomorrow and the day after, and I can bring you something nice. What about a pint of prawns? Or some jellied eels?'

She ignored my offer and started picking at her teeth with her blackened fingernails, as if she was sulking.

'I'm really sorry,' I went on. 'What about some tasty whelks, or a bone for Geezer?'

That only got her back up more. She rifled through the last of her blooms and then spat, 'S'pose you were off having fun, weren'tcha? Who's yer friend?'

Kate was standing beside me looking a bit puzzled by this harridan who was giving me such a hard time of it.

'She's a pal from Whitechapel, that's all,' I replied.

Well, that set her off again, mumbling something unkind about East End girls. I didn't think it was right for Pearlie to be saying that. In fact, it was a flaming liberty.

'Oh, give it a rest, Pearlie,' I shot back. 'If you must know, she's a hoister, like me. Maybe even better than me. So, she could have been a Seven Dials girl, but she just got born in the wrong parish, to the East, that's all. I think you owe her an apology, 'cos she's had a tough day.'

That made Pearlie change her tune. She smiled at Kate, which given the state of her teeth, wasn't much of an improvement on the cursing. 'Hoister?' she said warmly. 'You girls going to make a career of it, are you?' She started laughing, which was more of a cackle and that set her off on a bout of wheezing and coughing, so that I had to put the trunk down and give her a pat on the back.

'That's the plan,' I said, shrugging my shoulders.

'Well, well,' she said, 'I never thought you had it in you, Alice, but maybe you're more like Mary Carr and the Forty Thieves than I gave you credit for. I'll see you tomorrow. And don't you dare be late.'

'Who is Mary Carr and what are the Forty Thieves?' said Kate, as we picked up the trunk.

'Oh, it's some silly old story that Pearlie's been telling me about some urchins from the Dials back in the old days, who made a living out of hoisting and gave their gang a name, to make themselves sound good. I don't really know that much about them, to be honest, but I have a horrible feeling Pearlie is going to bore me half to death with every last detail of their exploits now, because I let her down today.'

That made us both laugh but I could have sworn as we rounded the corner into the cobbled terrace I called home, that I heard Pearlie sobbing in the distance.

The landlady wasn't too impressed with the fact that Kate had a huge trunkful of belongings, but she wasn't going to turn down the prospect of another girl paying rent while Lily was laid up in hospital.

She rustled us up a bit of bread and dripping in the scullery, which was a turn up for the books; you could barely get re-used tealeaves out of her on any other day of the week.

'Very nice, Mrs Dally,' I said, as we tucked in, and the hot dripping dribbled down my chin. She watched us eating for a while, and when I was picking the crumbs off the table, she thrust her hands deep into the pockets of her housecoat. 'There is the small matter of the rent . . .'

'Oh, that's fine,' said Kate, opening her purse. 'How much will it be for the week?'

'Month,' corrected Mrs Dally, simpering in her direction. 'I like my girls to pay by the month at first, just in case. No offence. That'll be seven shillings and sixpence.'

I opened my mouth to protest that she'd put the rent up because none of us had ever been asked to pay that much.

'It's to cover a little bit of what your poor dear friend Lily owes me,' she said, by way of explanation before I could say a word. 'I've been keeping her bed for her until now, as you know, but this ain't a charity, love. I just need to cover my costs.' Given that we had to fight her over the copper to get so much as a drop of hot water, I wasn't sure what extra costs she was on about. So she was having a laugh hiking up the price like that. But Kate just smiled as she handed over her money. 'It's fine by me, I'm just happy to have a roof over my head.'

'And will you be joining the others down at the jam factory?' Mrs Dally enquired. She did love a free pot of jam. Knowing her, she'd express a preference for the flavour that Kate should bring home. She was such a greedy cow.

'Yes,' I cut in before Kate could answer. 'I'll be getting that sorted with the foreman first thing in the morning. She'll have a job and she'll pay her rent, don't you worry, Mrs Dally.'

I wasn't planning on either of us staying in those jobs a moment longer than was necessary to keep the wolf from the door and I reckoned once I'd got the hang of those ridiculous bloomers that Kate had stitched, we'd make more by going shopping every day than we would bottling jam.

We climbed the narrow stairs to the bedroom, lugging the trunk between us. If you could have picked Mrs Dally's mangy old cat up by its tail and swung it in there, I swear I would have given you a pound. The other girls, Bertha and her best mate Gert, were loafing about, exhausted after another shift down at Pink's. Their bed was pushed up against one drab wall, while my bed was alongside the other, with a chair at the end. A single sash window overlooked the street, and we had a tiny dark wood wardrobe for our few belongings. It went without saying that the boards were bare. Mrs Dally spared us every home comfort.

'What the bloomin' heck have you got in there?' said Bertha, eyeing the trunk, which I shoved under the bed before she could get her hands on it.

'And who's this?' said Gert, sitting bolt upright, looking at Kate in a way which made it clear she wasn't particularly welcome. 'You ain't giving Lily's place away to her, are you?'

Bertha and Gert would snap Kate in two, like a twig, if they took a dislike to her.

'She needed to get away from the East End, sharpish, because of some trouble indoors, and she ain't interested in turfing Lily out of her place,' I soothed. 'She's just a girl in need of a roof over her head for a while. And we aren't the sort that would turn our back on her, are we?'

Bertha laid back down and went back to staring at the ceiling. 'S'pose not.'

Gert wasn't going to let it go that easily. 'But ain't that a bit of a liberty . . .?'

'If you must know, old Dally was thinking of giving Lily's bed away, the wicked mare,' I whispered, because the walls were paper thin, and voices carried. 'We had to get someone decent in to share with us or we might've had Lord only knows who bunking up with us by the end of the week,' I said. 'And when the time comes for Lily to come back home, Kate here will do the decent thing and find some more lodgings.'

''Course I will,' Kate chipped in. She pulled a bar of chocolate from her pocket. Knowing her, she'd probably nicked that as well. 'Anyone fancy some?'

I had to hand it to her, she knew how to get people on her side.

Gert didn't need to be asked twice. She took the bar, unwrapped it and broke off a large chunk, popping it in her mouth.

'Mmm, Cadbury's, my favourite,' she said. She gestured to the other bed. 'Make yourself at home, Kate.'

She undressed down to her chemise, pulling off those ridiculous hoister's bloomers which she hung on the bedpost, making me giggle. As she clambered onto the bed beside me, I couldn't help noticing a crescent-shaped red mark that ran the length of her left thigh. She made to cover it, embarrassed.

'It's so ugly,' she said. 'Johnny and his wife used to tell me it was the devil's mark because I was so wicked.'

'What a lot of nonsense!' I said. 'It makes you different, special, and don't you ever forget that, Kate.'

Later that evening, as we tucked ourselves top-to-toe under the thin blanket, I watched as she fell into a deep slumber. The curve of her hip was illuminated by the glow of a gas lamp in the street and gazing at her lying beside me, I felt happier than I could ever remember.

The next day, after spending more time than I'd care to mention listening to another one of Pearlie's stories about Mary Carr, I managed to grab some of the nicest blooms to take up to Lily, to make up for missing my visit.

The other girls had taken Kate for a celebratory drink for getting through the first shift at the factory, and being rewarded with a pot of strawberry jam for Mrs Dally.

Bertha and Gert had warmed to her after the chocolate she'd shared and they were quite protective, making sure she got a corned beef sarnie at lunchtime. I saw the way that Ernie looked at her when she clocked on, and it made me feel sick to the pit of my stomach. She was just his type: slim, pretty, delicate-looking. Except she wasn't. She was my friend and I was going to do everything I could to make sure that he kept his filthy paws off her while we were at Pink's.

I was hit by the usual smell of disinfectant as I pushed open the doors to the hospital ward, with my flowers safely tucked under my arm. The bed was neatly made, the crisp white sheets starched stiff, and the pillow plumped up. But there was no sign of Lily.

A hush fell over the room as I stood at the end of the bed, glancing around me, trying to work out where she'd gone. Only the sound of Matron's shoes squeaking towards me on the linoleum broke the silence. I remember the harsh thin line of her mouth softening, something in her eyes approaching kindness, and words coming out of her mouth, 'So sorry, dear', but then my head started spinning and my knees buckled underneath me. The last thing I recall was that cold, hard floor rushing up to greet me.

When I came to, I was propped up in a chair with a pillow behind my head, and Matron kneeling at my side, offering me a cup of sweet tea.

'Lily's dead, ain't she?' I said. I began to weep, for the first time in a very long time, crying with anger and rage at what had become of my beautiful friend, before I even understood the full horror of it.

'Don't upset yourself, you've had a nasty shock,' said Matron. She put the tea down on the bedside cabinet.

'What happened? When did it happen?' I said, tears spilling down my face. It hurt like hell when they reached my mouth because I'd bust my lip when I hit the floor. She held out a handkerchief to dab the blood from my mouth, but I pushed it away. I wanted to taste that blood, to feel it, because it reminded me that whatever had happened to Lily, I was still alive, to make it right.

'She got out of bed last night,' said Matron, in a whisper. 'She felt her way to the ward doors and pushed her way through them, and from there she made it along the corridor, to the stairwell and then . . .'

There was no need to say more. In my mind's eye I saw the horrible image of her body, lying broken and twisted, at the bottom of the stairs.

But still, I couldn't take it in. Perhaps they were mistaken? Perhaps it was another patient and not Lily. 'No, no!' I cried, 'She can't have . . .'

'It was too late when one of the orderlies found her,' said Matron softly. 'She'd gone, broken her neck in the fall. We're trying to trace relatives, but it seems that you were the closest thing to family that she had.'

I dried my eyes on the back of my hand. 'She lost her dad to heart trouble a few years back and her mum went not long after,' I said. 'If she had any other family, they weren't close because she never talked about them.' All she'd really had were her memories of Robert, her handsome soldier. At least she was with him now.

'If the body isn't claimed after a few days, well, we'll have to make the usual arrangements.' She shrugged her shoulders apologetically. We both knew what she was talking about. A pauper's funeral. Oh God, the shame of it. I wasn't having that, not for Lily.

'It's fine,' I said, sipping at the tea and pulling myself

together. 'Lily deserves better and, of course, she'll have a proper funeral. She wasn't in the workhouse, you know! She's got friends.'

Yes, she'd have a proper funeral, with flowers, a head-stone and everything. And I knew exactly who was going to pay for it, and not just with his own money. I'd already decided it would come at a price he'd remember for the rest of his life.

A hush fell over the pub as I walked in, my eyes red-rimmed from crying. I strolled up to the bar and ordered a whisky, drinking it so swiftly I felt it burning the back of my throat. The girls were gathered around the piano, and someone was hammering out 'My Old Man Said Follow The Van'. Bertha and Gert had linked arms and were kicking their legs up, and Kate was taking it all in, her face alive with the silliness of it. I expect she hadn't had this much fun in years. I didn't want to rain on their parade, but I knew I had to. I owed it to Lily, for starters. So, I waited until they'd finished singing their little ditty, and then I drew them into a huddle. 'Something terrible's happened,' I said, watching the look on their faces turn from jollity to horror. 'Lily's dead, she . . .' The words stuck in my throat. 'She's killed herself in the hospital.'

Bertha clapped her hand over her mouth to stifle a scream of disbelief and Gert just mouthed, 'How?' I tried to explain it the best I could, but I kept stopping to sob. A few of the fellas at the bar started glancing over in our direction, wondering what on earth was going on.

And that's when he walked in.

They say animals hunt in packs and can communicate without words. The look that Gert and Bertha shot me when Ernie strolled up to the bar and ordered himself a nice pint of bitter was like that.

'I won't be long, ladies,' I said, standing up and smoothing my skirt down. 'I'm just off to have a little word in our friend's ear. I expect we'll both feel like some fresh air in about five minutes or so, if you catch my drift.'

Bertha nodded and she and Gert started gathering up their things. Kate looked a bit confused.

'Take her with you,' I said, 'but keep her out of it, and keep her safe.' Bertha was from a family where arguments were settled with fists. Her mum was one of the wastepaper factory women who had fights for pennies on a Sunday at the top of the street, not just to settle scores, but for laughs. Bertha was cut from the same cloth and Gert, well, let's just say I wouldn't mess with her. She wouldn't have looked out of place in a boxing ring.

I sashayed over towards the bar. I cannot tell a lie, it wasn't easy for me in my current mood, but I did it just the same, wiggling my hips a little. Ernie let out a low whistle as I approached, draping my arm around his shoulder.

'Buy a girl a drink, why don'tcha?' I chimed.

He looked me up and down, taking in my pretty rosebud print blouse, his eyes travelling slowly over my chest. That churned my guts.

'That's a pretty top,' he said, brushing some of the beery froth from his moustache. 'Makes you look almost feminine, I'd say.' Some wisecrack at the end of the bar chipped in. 'Oh, leave orf Ernie!'

'No offence, love,' he said, smirking. 'He just don't appreciate beauty like yours. Now, what can I do for you?'

'It's just, I've been thinking, now that my mate's not at work anymore, I wondered if there might be more opportunities for me?' Just saying that brought tears to my eyes, but I had started off down this path and catching the look of glee on his stupid little face made me even more determined to see it through.

'I didn't think you'd ever be knocking on my door for help,' he said, slipping a hand around my waist and giving me a little squeeze. 'But here you are. While the cat's away the mice will play, eh? How is Lottie?'

'It's Lily,' I said, swallowing hard. 'She ain't doing so great. In fact, she's taken a turn for the worse.'

'That's right, of course it was Lily,' he said. 'Such a shame, she had a lovely, pretty face. You will send her my best, won't you?'

'I was kind of hoping you could tell her yourself, before too much longer,' I replied coldly. In the corner, someone started playing the piano again and the half of the pub that was still sober enough to stand started jigging about and singing at the top of their voices.

I struggled to make myself heard over the din. 'I have some great ideas for increasing productivity, but it's so noisy in here. Why don't we step outside, and we can talk in private?'

'Blimey,' he said, with a twinkle in his eye. 'You're keen, aren't you? I never thought you were the type, Anna.'

'It's Alice,' I shouted, 'And I think you'll find I'm full of surprises. Follow me.'

We strolled out of the pub together and I led him around to the back alley by the bins because in my heart of hearts, I knew that was where blokes like him deserved to end up, with the rubbish. I let him push me back against the wall, feeling the hardness of him protruding through his cheap suit. We stood eye-to-eye and I could smell the beer on his breath, as he lifted the hem of my skirt with one hand and started to unbutton his fly with the other.

'Oh, you are a dirty cow, aren't you?' he leered. 'I bet you can't wait for what I've got to give you, good and . . .' But he didn't finish his sentence because Bertha smacked him around the back of the head with an empty bottle, felling him like a rotten tree. As he lay at my feet, I kicked him in the ribs, hard, making him puke his pint into the gutter, while Gert swung her carpet bag at his head. At one point, I heard something crack, as all three of us put the boot in. I think it was his ribs, or possibly his jaw, but I can't say I minded which it was, really. His blood spilled out onto the cobbles as he groaned in agony. I bent down and removed his fat wallet from his jacket pocket, helping myself to the crisp notes inside. I even relieved him of his last few shillings. Those would pay for the flowers.

'That's for Lily,' I said, giving him another kick, right where it hurt. He howled, glancing up at me with a mixture of disbelief and pain etched on his features. I towered over him as he grovelled at my feet, curling himself into a ball.

'She's gone for good. And if you breathe a word of this to anyone, I swear to God, next time you'll be joining her!' I spat.

We marched back home to our terrace with our heads held high, hooting with mirth about the beating we'd dished out to Ernie and how he'd had it coming. But Kate dawdled along behind us and didn't join in with the chatter. In fact, when I caught a glimpse of her, as Bertha was reliving the moment she'd clubbed Ernie with a bottle, she almost jumped with fright.

'You girls go on in and put your feet up,' I said to Bertha and Gert. 'Me and Kate'll go and have a look at the river for a minute.' They glanced in her direction. She'd gone white as a sheet.

87

'A bit of night air might bring some colour back to your cheeks, Kate,' said Gertha, with a look of concern. 'We'll put the kettle on when you get back.'

I fell into step beside her, watching closely, seeing the fear in her eyes.

I reached out to give her a hug, but she brushed my arm away. 'I don't like violence, Alice,' she said coldly. 'You scared me, how much you seemed to like it, how easy it was for you.'

Her words cut me in a way I couldn't fathom. We had to be prepared to stand up to men who crossed us, or we'd end up in the gutter. Surely she could understand that? But I didn't want her to be afraid, not of me.

'I'd never hurt you,' I whispered, feeling a flush of shame rising in my cheeks. I wanted to tell her how much I cared about her, that I'd look after her and put myself in danger rather than let anyone harm a hair on her head. But just the thought of saying that made me feel as if the pavement beneath my feet was giving way and I might disappear down one of the cracks. The words that were spinning around my head wouldn't come out right. So, instead, I said, 'You're my pal and my partner in crime, Kate. You'll always be safe with me.'

I swallowed hard. I didn't want her to disapprove of me and I didn't understand why I was so upset. The thought that she might not want to be close to me, that she'd seen a side of me she despised, was more hurtful than anything I'd ever known. I wasn't like the brute who'd beaten her in the East End! I'd been standing up for Lily, if only I could make her understand . . .

The sound of our footsteps echoed on the cobbles and the whistling of the lightermen on the boats bobbing along the river carried through the night air. Kate leaned in closer, her dark curls falling on my shoulder, her face upturned, gazing at me. She took my hand and the ground beneath my feet felt firm once more.

'I trust you, Alice,' she said.

CHAPTER 8

MARY

Mayfair, December 1899

They say a year's a long time in London.

For me, it felt like a lifetime, and a good one at that, because now I had the best of everything. I'd gone from scraping a living in the slums to living like a lady, in appearances at least. My soft woollen coat had a fine astrakhan collar, and I wore a felt hat with a wide brim and three ostrich feathers in it as I sauntered along Oxford Street towards Selfridges, mingling with the well-to-do folk. My waist was pulled in neatly by the finest whalebone corset; the days of me wearing a tatty liberty bodice were long gone. I dressed like one of the quality now.

I can't quite recall when they started calling me 'Queen' around the Seven Dials, but now everyone knew I could get fine things for a very reasonable price and that won me more respect than any fella. I had an elegant air about me, which I cultivated by studying Lady Harcourt whenever I went to sit for her. She was still painting and drawing me once a week, dressing me up in filthy rags and torn dresses. But now I really was play-acting my despair because my life had changed for the better all thanks to one thing: hoisting. I don't know whether she sensed it, but she took great pleasure in making me stand in awkward positions for hours, without a rest, as if she wanted to make my life as difficult as possible, to make the expressions of misery on my face even more real. It did cross my mind not to bother showing up, but she'd made it clear that if I didn't make myself available, she'd send her butler and maybe even the police looking for me, because she was paying for my time. And she never had a kind word to say to me, so it was always a relief to get back to my new career as a top hoister.

Polly turned out to be a reliable and daring deputy, and between us we recruited around half a dozen other girls from the Dials into the Forty Thieves, swearing them to secrecy in our derelict hideout, just as we had done at the beginning.

My skills with the sewing needle came in very handy and before long I'd conjured up some petticoats with large pockets sewn onto them for us to stash our loot. I cut slits into our skirts, so we could simply slip whatever we'd pinched into our underwear without being spotted. Polly had another notion, to create large pockets which we'd hang from a belt on our waistband. Those were useful for nicking bulkier items, such as fur stoles and mittens. We worked in teams of two or three, with one girl creating a distraction as the other two pilfered to their heart's content. With my hair curled and pinned, just as Lady Harcourt did hers, I was even able to make money disappear from the till and away into my tresses. That was quite a trick and it made Polly giggle so much the first time I did it in Selfridges that we almost got caught.

Any time that the cozzers came calling – and they'd only come around the Dials in pairs, for their own safety – we'd be spirited away into people's sculleries, hidden under beds or shooed away down back alleys until the coast was clear. They might've had their suspicions about us and why we were dressed so la-di-da, but they never caught us at it. That was all part of the fun.

'It's like having a proper family, ain't it?' said Polly, as we counted through piles of coins from the hoisted goods we'd sold on. With her share, she made a point of putting food on the table for her brothers and sisters, and before long, her mum was strong enough to come home from the hospital for the first time in weeks.

I watched as Polly came back from the bakery with an armful of treats to celebrate, only to be cornered by her dad, swaying from drink, in the doorway to their tenement. News of Polly's good fortune had reached his stupid ears, it seemed.

She stopped dead in her tracks but in an instant, he'd knocked a cake clean out of her hand. In the house behind him, I could hear one of her younger sisters starting to whimper. It was a routine they knew only too well, with him dishing out the beatings.

I stepped out of the alleyway towards him, with the rest of the Forty Thieves girls behind me, and out of nowhere, housewives who'd always hurried off indoors or turned a blind eye to his bullying were also at my side. For once, the women of the Dials were going to stand up to this beast of a man and pride swelled in my chest as I realised that my gang had given them strength.

'You'd better be on your way,' I said, glaring at him. There was quite a crowd of us by now.

'You and whose army?' he scoffed, seizing hold of Polly. She shook herself free, her face contorting with disdain.

'*Our* army, the Forty Thieves,' she said, her chin tilting up to him in defiance. 'You ain't welcome here no more, you drunken oaf. Hoppit!'

He hesitated for an instant, clinging to the rotting wood of the door frame, while he sized up his chances against this crowd of angry young girls and women, with Polly and me leading the charge. Then his shoulders drooped a little as he straightened his grubby neckerchief, thrusting his hands deep into the pockets of his trousers, as he slunk away, with our jeers ringing in his ears.

Polly beamed at me and mouthed, 'Thanks, Mary.'

Being a hoister had changed things for her, for the better, there was no doubt about it. She was a mere strip of a girl but in that moment, facing up to the man who'd tormented her all these years, she was a giant.

My ma was happy as a skylark with the upturn in my fortunes, although she'd swear blind that she never knew where the money came from when she was down the boozer. 'Oh, Mary's such a lucky child!' she'd crow, buying everyone a round. 'Do you know she found a ten-pound note only the other day?' And the whole pub would drink to that, at my expense. I can't say I minded because a tight-lipped community was what I relied on to keep me and my girls out of jail.

One wintry afternoon, after a lovely morning's spree up in Gamages on High Holborn, I made my way home to keep my appointment to go and sit for Lady Harcourt up in Mayfair. The fog was already starting to build as the light began to dim in that way that it did when Christmas was drawing near, and the days were getting shorter. Hot chestnut sellers were stamping their feet and warming their fingers on their braziers on street corners as I returned to the Dials, to change into more simple attire. These days, the only time I put on clothes which were fitting for me as a slum girl was when I was pretending, for Lady Harcourt's sake. Jem was waiting for me on the doorstep, and he toddled away from my sister Ada's grasp to greet me.

'Nice of you to show up,' she scowled. 'Some of us have proper jobs to go to.'

Oh, how she hated me out earning her ten-to-one and wielding so much power around the Dials. It stuck right in her craw, like a fishbone that wouldn't go down. Now, she had to act as the nursemaid to Jem while I went out hoisting with my gang, because Ma wouldn't have it any other way.

I pulled out a lovely red silk neckerchief and handed it to her.

'This is just a token of my gratitude,' I said, smiling sweetly. It was exactly what Lady Harcourt said to me when she handed me my pay, only she never cracked a grin in my direction.

'Oh, I can't stand it!' cried Ada, stamping her foot. 'Stop pretending to be all hoity-toity! I know who you really are, Mary Carr, and you ain't no lady.' She snatched it from me, just the same, and fastened it around her neck to keep out the bitter cold. Then, she pulled on the beautiful gaberdine cape I'd pinched for her the other week and headed off to the laundry, without so much as a word of thanks.

'Don't bite the hand that feeds you, Ada!' I shouted at her departing back.

Then I scooped Jem up and cuddled him, smelling his sweet, babyish curls.

He was plump and healthy and had a lovely pair of sturdy boots and fine wool stockings to keep him warm. I made sure that he, above all of us, got the best cuts of meat and the softest blankets in his new cot. I was planning to get him a goose-feather eiderdown for Christmas, to keep him nice and snug. Providing for him was my biggest delight and made all the risks I was taking worthwhile. I felt a warm glow of pride about it.

He still loved riding in his crate on wheels, and clambered on board, ready for us to set off. The time we spent on those walks was so precious. Each week, he'd notice something new, something to bring a smile to his innocent little face.

The streets of Soho were bustling with people running errands between shops decked with holly and mistletoe, but beneath the gleaming windows filled with tempting goods, I witnessed the other side of London. Men with fob watches dangling from their waistcoats and ladies whose hands were warmed by fur-lined gloves moved well away from the pavement-dwellers – the beggars in rags, the half-starved child with sunken cheeks, the woman with tattered skirts and a black eye from last night's beating, who gazed mindlessly ahead as she tried to sell the only thing of value she owned to any willing stranger, up the nearest back alley.

I opened my purse to all of them, dropping pennies into upturned palms. This was not the happy poverty that Her Ladyship was always going on about. This was the real face of the Seven Dials, founded on utter despair, want and hunger; robbed of hope and ignored by those who ventured to the clubs and theatres that bordered this miserable swamp of human struggle, to laugh and celebrate their good fortune.

I knew I couldn't change it. Gawd knows, I'd been a few farthings away from the gutter myself when my ma had drunk the best part of her wages and the rent man came calling. So, sharing a little of my wealth seemed the right thing to do, even if it only bought them a bag full of chestnuts or a bellyful of beer to take the chill off the evening.

★

The gas lamps were already hissing, casting their eerie, yellowish glow through the fog as we trundled through the neat garden squares of Mayfair. Hedges and trees were half shrouded in mist, and the sound of horses' hooves echoed on the cobbles as I hurried towards Lady Harcourt's grand house. She hated me to be late and the housekeeper would use that as an excuse to pull my hair or pinch me harder than usual.

I rapped on the servants' entrance before gingerly opening the door into the kitchen below stairs to find Maisie, the scullery maid, smiling at us, and the cook red-faced and fussing over a plate of mince pies.

Maisie swiped one when the cook turned around to take another batch out of the oven, popping it into the pocket of her apron as she followed me and Jem up to the entrance hallway.

'Is he hungry?' she asked, patting him on the head as he climbed slowly up the narrow staircase, his fat palms pressing against the walls to steady himself.

'I don't think so,' I said. 'He had some day-old buns earlier.'

That was a fib. I couldn't remember the last time I'd got up early to queue for stale bread. Now we could afford to eat cakes and fresh loaves whenever we fancied, and I made sure that Jem got lots of treats.

She looked a bit disappointed at that because I knew she loved feeding Jem.

'But he's bound to be hungry afterwards,' I added quickly. 'So perhaps you could keep it for him 'til later?'

Now, I wasn't exactly missing the housekeeper, the evil old cow, but I was beginning to wonder where she'd got to as we made our way up the grand staircase and along the landing to the studio. She usually stood sentry at the top of the stairs to make sure I hadn't brought any dirt in, like I did the first time I came to the house.

Maisie lowered her voice to a whisper. 'She's tending to the mistress, proper sick she is, with a burning pain behind her eyes. She can hardly lift her head off the pillow. Miss White is keeping watch over her.'

'But who will do the painting?' I asked.

The door to the studio swung open and a tall, handsome man was standing there, paintbrush in hand, his eyes twinkling with amusement.

'I will,' he replied.

His hair was in a side parting but even that failed to tame the unruly mop of curls which tumbled over his smooth brow and framed his chiselled jaw. He wore a high, white collar that was just visible beneath the blue painter's smock, which fell almost to his knees. I found myself blushing stupidly, right to the roots of my hair, as he ushered me inside.

'So, you must be my dear wife's latest subject?' he said, raising an eyebrow, a smile playing on his lips.

'Yes, Your Lordship,' I stammered, as Jem hid behind my legs. I'd never seen the master of the house before, although Her Ladyship had spoken of his artistic talents with great pride. He was a man whose paintings hung in the finest galleries of the land, so she'd told me.

'Mary, isn't it?'

I nodded mutely.

'And is this your little brother? He's a fine fellow, isn't he?' He knelt down to get a closer look at Jem, who rewarded him with a chuckle, before toddling off to the toy box in the corner. I undid my coat, fumbling a bit, and then there was an awkward silence, broken only by the sound of Jem tipping buttons out of the box and onto the floor, which made Lord Harcourt laugh.

'Well, now he has made himself at home, I suppose we'd best get on with this painting, hadn't we?'

The canvas was already on the easel, and I caught a glimpse of the unfinished picture, which was of me, dressed in a tattered red calico skirt and blouse, clasping a basketful of violets, looking downcast. Oh gawd, how I hated that outfit because the cotton was so scratchy.

'But you will need to change?' The question hung in the air.

'Yes, Your Lordship, that's usually the way,' I replied, grateful that I was able to turn my back and quickly make my way to the modesty screen in the corner, where the basketful of ragged clothes was stored. My cheeks were burning hot with embarrassment as I quickly stripped to my underwear, unlaced my corset and pulled on my slum girl outfit, leaving the top few buttons undone, as Her Ladyship had instructed me, even though it exposed my neck and chest. Then, I pulled on the straw bonnet she wanted me to wear and fastened it under my chin.

'Ah yes,' he said as I emerged from behind the screen, gazing at me. 'That's much more fitting for a flower seller, isn't it? How long do you usually sit for?'

'I ain't exactly sure, Your Lordship,' I replied. For some reason, in front of him, I felt half naked and I wished I could cover myself with a shawl. But with Her Ladyship, being an artist's model was so boring, I let time pass me by, daydreaming or just watching Jem play. 'Her Ladyship usually spends a couple of hours or so, I'd wager.'

He was already dabbling his paintbrushes in the paints as I took up my position with a basket of flowers. He hummed to himself a bit as he worked. I was supposed to be staring at the floor, looking miserable, but I couldn't stop myself glancing up occasionally, just to catch a glimpse of him. He worked much more quickly than Her Ladyship, who took forever, making tiny, little brushstrokes with agonized cries when she got it wrong. He swept over that canvas like lightning and after an hour, he rang the bell and sent for afternoon tea. That had never happened before; Her Ladyship had never offered me so much as a sip of water, even in high summer.

Yet, here was Maisie bearing a gleaming tray and silver tea service, stuffed with the daintiest little sandwiches and even a glass of milk for Jem. She bobbed low in a curtsey with it, which seemed like a feat of magic, because not one drop of liquid was spilled, before she laid the tray carefully on the rickety old table by the bay window. I stood there like a spare part, not daring to move, let alone sit and have some refreshment. I knew my place well enough.

'Would you like some tea?' he said, wiping his hands clean on a rag. Even so, there were still spots of paint on the backs of his hands, all the way up to his wrists. I couldn't help noticing how soft his hands looked and his nails were so clean and perfectly tidy, not like any of the blokes round our way. He didn't have rough workman's hands. I found myself wondering what it would be like to be touched by him.

He pulled out one of the old wooden chairs for me to sit on, before doing so himself. That made me want to giggle; the sight of me dressed in rags and him in this posh house, sitting at a table so creaky it would be right at home in the Seven Dials.

I took my place opposite him, and he murmured, 'You are so very perfect.'

I was speechless at that.

'If you say so, Your Lordship,' I stuttered, meeting his gaze.

'Well, I do say so. Your skin is so luminescent and your hair so dark and striking; you wouldn't look out of place in a Titian.'

I had no idea what he was on about, but I think he was trying to pay me a compliment. I wasn't used to that, not least from someone of his standing.

'Oh, forgive me, I'm not trying to embarrass you, Mary,' he said, pouring the tea and handing me a cup perched upon a delicate-looking saucer. 'I speak as an artist, admiring the qualities you have. Your neck is as long and beautiful as that of a swan and your beauty is pure and unsullied by all the fripperies used by women to trick the opposite sex. Might you consider sitting for me as well?

'I have a studio in Piccadilly, which is a much better space than this. You could bring your brother and I'd pay you handsomely for your time.'

I swallowed hard and thought of a reply, but my heart was pounding.

'That's very decent of you, Your Lordship,' was all I managed to say, before taking a sip of the tea, which was scalding hot, in spite of the milk he had poured in for me. I did what I'd always done at home and tipped some into the saucer to cool it a little, which made him guffaw. I felt stupid then, because I hadn't realised that the upper classes would never do such a thing, which was frowned upon in polite society.

But do you know what he did then, that toff painter?

He blooming well followed suit and poured his tea into the saucer too, just to make me feel better. That was when I knew it for sure.

I was quite fond of Lord Wilberforce Harcourt.

'I'd be glad to sit for you, Your Lordship,' I added, with a smile.

'That's very good, very good indeed,' he replied, offering Jem a sandwich as he toddled up to join us. 'But there's one thing I must ask above all else and I am sorry to have to impose this on you, Mary.'

I watched him for a moment, as he chewed his sandwich thoughtfully.

Then, he added, in a whisper, 'It has to be our little secret because I want it be a surprise for Lady Harcourt.'

'I understand, Your Lordship,' I said, lowering my gaze.

For some reason, it was a secret I was only too willing to keep.

CHAPTER 9

MARY

Piccadilly, December 1899

Logs crackled in the grate as I warmed my fingers by
the fire.

Even my fox fur muff couldn't keep the chill away and
I could barely feel my toes after walking along the ice-
covered pavements from the Seven Dials to Lord Harcourt's
studio. Through a huge, arched window, the sky over
London was leaden with snow clouds, but he radiated
happiness at the sight of me and it was like the summer
sun coming out, right in the middle of winter.

'Here,' he said, handing me a glass of sherry. 'This will
warm you up, then we really must get to work.'

I sipped at it, gazing at the flickering flames, pondering
how much my life had changed, while he busied himself
with his paintbrushes and his canvas. His pictures were
much bigger than anything that Lady Harcourt attempted,
standing five feet tall at least. His studio was strewn with
paintings and works in progress, pots of paint, scraps of
paper, bottles of white spirit, palettes and all sorts of props
to set the scene he required. It was messy and chaotic, but
I didn't mind that either because he was kind to me, which
was more than could be said for his wife. The more time
I spent in her presence, the more I noticed her pinched
features, her long, pointed nose and the haughty look that

always came before some barbed comment aimed in my direction. He had a face which was pleasant to look at, and I must confess, I had made quite a study of it.

It was my fourth session as his model and although some of the things he wanted me to wear seemed ridiculous, I looked forward to posing for him, although the time he made me stand there all afternoon draped in a white sheet because he said it was what Greek women wore in the olden days did make me chuckle.

I even got Ada and the other girls to look after Jem, so that I wouldn't be distracted during my modelling sessions, and I could focus on what Lord Harcourt wanted me to do. He had a way of looking at me, of appreciating me, that made me feel different, chosen, special even.

'There's a dress behind the screen for you today – it's velvet, so you should feel quite warm in it,' he said as I finished my drink. He was excited, like a schoolboy with a new spinning top. 'I can't wait to see how you look – the colour should set off your hair in a way that will be divine to paint.'

I nodded, wincing slightly as I unlaced my boots and wiggled my toes, which were still numb. Behind the screen, I spied the most magnificent, emerald-green velvet gown, with draped sleeves, and my heart skipped a beat. Picking it up, I held it to my cheek for a moment, feeling the softness of the fabric. On the floor lay a pair of velvet slippers sewn with golden thread with the initials *LDH* on the front. It was heavenly to pop my feet into them as I unbuttoned my jacket, slipping out of my blouse and unfastening the waistband of my skirt. I stepped into the dress and pulled it up, smoothing it over my arms. It was heavier and more expensive than anything I'd ever worn before and fell so low at the front that it exposed the top of my bosom. I clasped my hands to cover myself as I shuffled out from behind the screen, feeling embarrassed about how much of me was on show.

He glanced up at me and a look crossed his face, a different look to the amusement he sometimes had when he saw me, or the concentration that made his brows knit together when he was painting.

My insides did a somersault as he continued to gaze in my direction.

There was no mistaking it.

This was desire, glowing like the embers in the grate.

My hair was pinned and curled up, with just a few strands falling around my face, but he came to my side and freed it, letting it tumble in waves over my shoulders. I'd only managed to button the dress to the waist before stepping into it, leaving it open at the back.

'Turn around,' he murmured. 'Let me do that for you.'

He stood so close, I could smell cigars on his breath as his fingers worked their way up to the nape of my neck, button by button. Closing my eyes, I became aware of his delicate touch. A tingle of excitement began to build in the pit of my stomach, and there was an unfamiliar, warm sensation between my legs, floating and pulling at the same time, whenever he brushed against my skin, with tiny strokes, like a painter putting the finishing touches to his creation.

'Come and stand closer to the fire,' he said. 'I can still feel the chill on you.'

I followed him across the room, the velvet swishing around my ankles, watching closely as he took something down from the mantelpiece. It was a black box, made of the finest leather, and as he flipped it open, I saw it was lined with red silk. Nestling there was a diamond necklace. He held it up and it began glinting, almost dancing, in the firelight, pulsating with a rhythm of its own. I gasped with longing, feeling the pull of those precious stones through my very core, my legs weak, my eyes widening in wonder.

In an instant, he had placed it around my neck, the row of diamonds caressing my skin and the heaviest gem suspended between my breasts. I arched my back with pleasure, moaning softly as he pulled me to him, covering my mouth with his own.

Now, I don't want you to think I'm one of the kind of girls who will just go weak for a fella, 'cos I ain't. I'd watched women from the Seven Dials lose their marbles over a bloke many times down the boozer, and Lord Harcourt was handsome and as intoxicating as too much gin, but it was the stones that had me in their thrall. It was like magic, what they did to me. I wasn't a girl from the slums when I wore them, I was a ballet dancer, a swan, a Greek goddess, perhaps even a princess.

When he took me in his arms, I was hot like the flames of the fire, until he cooled me with his lovemaking. And all the while, as he nudged his way inside me, I watched the diamonds twinkling, burning with passion I'd never known until now, feeling waves of pleasure wash over me. He lost himself in that moment in my arms, but I was already in ecstasy over the beauty of the diamonds, gasping, wanting more.

'You look so beautiful, Mary,' he said, as we lay together on a chaise longue by the fireside afterwards, the dress in a crumpled heap at my feet. He twirled a lock of my hair around his fingers. 'But I hope you don't feel I have taken advantage of you? That was never my intention, please believe me. It was never my intention . . .' He had such an earnest look about him, like a puppy, that I almost felt sorry for him. 'I only wanted to paint you to show my wife how perfectly exquisite her taste in models is. She has so little confidence in her abilities, I was hoping to show her that by finding you, she'd selected someone that painters at the Royal Academy would appreciate.'

I shrugged my shoulders. I didn't particularly care who saw me in paintings; they were all posh folk, cut from the same cloth, as far as I could tell. And I didn't think he'd taken advantage of the situation because it wasn't as if he'd forced me. I was old enough to marry and curious enough to want to know what it felt like, the things that I knew men and women got up to together, but it was the diamonds I really fancied.

'I really would like to paint you today, if you have the time?' he ventured.

He poured us both another glass of sherry. 'Fine by me, Your Lordship,' I replied. Nobody around the Seven Dials was the boss of me. I could come and go as I pleased, and I didn't want to leave, not yet, because I didn't want to be parted from those gems. I stood up and began to pull on the velvet dress. He gazed at me thoughtfully as he sipped at his drink, and I touched the diamonds at my neck. 'They suit you, truly they do, it's as if they come alive on you, more than on . . .'

He stopped himself but I pursued it.

'Begging your pardon, Your Lordship, but whose are they?'

Something flickered across his face then, just as it started to snow outside and the wind whistled down the chimney; it was a look approaching guilt. 'They belong to my wife, as do the slippers.'

'Just tilt your chin down a little, but try to meet my gaze, Mary.'

I was standing on a podium in the middle of the studio, watching the gas lamps on the wall throw eerie shapes up towards the ornate plasterwork on the ceiling. The green velvet dress fell in soft drapes from my waist, puddling around my feet, which were still encased in Lady Dorothy Harcourt's fancy slippers. The necklace at my throat glinted and twinkled, each stone more beautiful than the next, as Lord Harcourt worked in a frenzy to capture it all on canvas.

'Stretch your neck a little, that's perfect,' he said, squinting as he raised his paintbrush. 'Oh, your skin is so pale, and your hair is truly gleaming in this light,' he said, daubing yet more paint. My legs ached from standing and I hadn't eaten since breakfast, but I did not want to trouble him for a rest because that would distract him from his work.

'This will be the most beautiful thing I have ever created,' he murmured to himself, dipping the brushes in fresh paint again and again, as he returned to the canvas, applying the colour in broad strokes.

The hours ticked by, and it was pitch black outside by the time he finally helped me down. I almost crumpled into his arms with exhaustion. I had a horrible sinking feeling, not at being parted from him, but at the prospect of having to take off the necklace. I touched it, longingly, stroking each gem, as he led me to the canvas to show me the portrait he had painted.

I gasped. There I was, resplendent in emerald velvet, my black hair cascading over my pale skin, with my neck so elegant and my gaze enticing. At my throat, the necklace sparkled and danced with its own light; a light he had captured so perfectly on the canvas. It was breathtaking.

'Mary,' he said, breaking into a broad smile as he dipped his hand into the front pocket of his painter's smock, pulling out a sparkling diamond ring, which he presented to me. 'Consider this a token of my gratitude and affection.'

He planted a little kiss on my cheek.

'For you, my dear, are my Queen of Diamonds.'

CHAPTER 10

ALICE

Elephant and Castle, July 1923

Lily's coffin was covered with flowers that hot summer's morning, as we laid her to rest. It was the kind of day which was full of promise, with a warmth in the air and ripe peaches on the barrows down the market. Yet here we were, saying goodbye to our friend as the sun climbed high in the cloudless sky over London.

Pearlie had done us proud with the floral display, but as me and the girls from our lodgings watched the coffin being lowered into the ground, I couldn't get rid of the sense that I'd failed my friend. After the vicar said his final prayers, I tipped the gravedigger a shilling to keep the grave tidy. I still had enough cash left over for a proper headstone for her but even that felt like a cop-out. And as we shuffled off together, arm-in-arm, to get back to work, wiping away our tears, I felt a stab of guilt at leaving Lily behind.

Ernie was waiting at the factory gates, cracking his knuckles, as if he meant business. He was nursing a fat lip and the bruises on his cheekbones were darkening to a deep purple. Now, Ernie was a proud man, too proud to say he'd been beaten senseless and robbed by a bunch of jam factory girls, but I knew from the look in his eye that he was as angry as a bulldog chewing a wasp.

He let the others pass, tutting at them for being late, making threats to dock their pay, but when it came to me and Kate, he blocked the way, stretching his arm out to stop us getting by. Then he took great pleasure in producing our clocking-on cards from the pocket of his foreman's duster coat. Slowly, very slowly, he ripped them to shreds before throwing the pieces at our feet. I didn't bat an eyelid, I wasn't afraid of him, but I heard Kate gasp behind me.

He leaned forward, so that I caught the faintest whiff of his shaving cream, and whispered, 'There's no room in this factory for the likes of you and your little friend. So, you're fired, see?'

'You won't get away with this, Ernie,' I said, squaring up to him. 'You know you deserved the beating you got. The score needed to be settled.'

He clenched his fists at the reminder of his humiliation at the hands of a bunch of women.

Kate tugged at my sleeve. 'Leave him, Alice, he just ain't worth it. We'll manage on our own.' I turned to see her gazing up at me, her face so full of warmth and determination that it almost made my heart jump for joy. But I knew, deep down, that we both had a lot to learn about thieving for a living and if we were going to make a real go of it, we needed more time to put a plan together.

I was putting a brave face on it, eyeballing him and standing my ground, but at that moment, there was a loud wolf whistle from behind Ernie's back, and Bertha and Gert came marching out of Pink's, bringing half the workforce with them.

Ernie turned as red as a vat of strawberry jam at the sight of them, with steam practically shooting out of his ears. 'What in the name of God Almighty do you think you're doing?' he cried, as a long line of girls walked past, glaring at him, with their arms folded.

'We're voting with our feet!' said Bertha, smirking at him as she came to my side. 'The whole shopfloor knows what you did to Lily, and they don't want to work for the likes of you, Ernie, seeing as you're taking it out on our chum Alice and her new friend.'

'That's right,' said Gert, prodding him so hard in the chest he practically fell over. 'Stop picking on us women! We're on strike!'

'But you can't do that!' he said, throwing up his hands in despair. 'You can't just walk out of the factory. What about my quotas?'

'You can stick your quotas where the sun doesn't shine, Ernie,' said Bertha, with a grin. 'I'm sure you'll think of something to tell the bosses. Meanwhile, me and the girls have got a bit of a thirst, so we're off down the boozer.'

'I'll have to fire the lot of you!' he shouted.

'Oh, don't be daft, Ernie,' said Gert, over her shoulder. 'You can't do that because then all your jam would spoil, wouldn't it? We'll give you a bit of time to think things through.'

Ernie's mouth fell open in shock and he stood there, his eyes wide with amazement, as all the jam factory girls from Pink's filed past him. A few of them took the opportunity to stick two fingers up in his direction. Someone started whistling 'Knees up Mother Brown' and by the time we reached the pub the girls were singing it at the top of their voices, dancing over the cobbles and shrieking with laughter, as if they were on a day out.

That was the kind of wake Lily deserved and I was proud to say we gave it to her.

★

'So,' said Bertha, as she sipped a port and lemon, and the landlord refilled everyone's glasses, 'what's the plan, Alice?'

'You need to give Ernie an hour to cool his heels and then get this lot back to work,' I said, eyeing the girls who were knocking back sherries like it was Christmas, leaning on the bar and spending all their wages on drink.

'Well, I, for one, ain't going back,' said Gert, slamming her half-pint of beer down on the table in disgust. 'He can go and whistle for it, as far as I'm concerned.'

'Me neither,' said Bertha. 'So, are you two going to let us in on whatever it is the pair of you are up to? What've you got in that trunk under the bed?'

Kate grinned at me, and I knew then she'd given me her approval to tell them our secrets.

'Me and Kate here have got a special sort of talent,' I began.

'You ain't acrobats or magicians, are you?' said Bertha, without a trace of irony. 'Thinking of running away to join the circus?'

I almost burst out laughing at that, but I'd already noticed that there were two girls sitting at the next table who were eavesdropping on our entire conversation. I lowered my voice. 'Do I look like a blooming contortionist or someone who's going to pull a rabbit from a top hat?' I said to Bertha. 'No, it's a talent which means we can earn easy money, a lot of money, perhaps.'

That got Gert's attention. She loved a flutter on the gee-gees or the dogfights or anything that could bring her a quick return. 'If it's a money-making scheme and better than working for that tosser, Ernie, I'm in,' she said, leaning forward eagerly.

'It's hoisting,' I said in a whisper, as one of the girls on the next table was craning her neck so far towards us that she could practically sip my drink. She had fine features and was slender, with a kind of elegance about her. Her huge, dark eyes seemed to eat up her face, which was framed by a cloud of jet-black hair. 'We are shoplifting, liberating expensive goods to sell to people round our way who have a liking for things they can only get on the never-never from the tallyman or perhaps, not at all.

'My question is, why should we let the tallyman, with his ludicrous repayments, get away with it? Why should he have the run of these streets when we can get in on the action and offer women a better price? You end up paying ten times the cost for a bleeding tea towel or a bag of clothes pegs off his cart! If we set up a proper thieving operation, we can undercut him and give housewives lovely things that they really want, at a fair price, with no interest, and still make plenty of money for ourselves.'

I could see that Gert liked the sound of that because her ma had got so behind with the rent repayments when she was a girl. Her ma had to get her leg over to make up the shortfall because of the need to keep up with the tallyman and his dues. Now, I'm not judging her for that, plenty of women did it, but Gert's dad came home from the docks early and caught them at it. He whacked her ma so hard that she fell against the fireplace. She was as deaf as a post in one ear because of it.

Bertha's face fell. 'Oh, I dunno, Alice, I'm not light-fingered or quick enough to get away with pinching stuff . . .'

'That's fine,' I said. 'We need lookouts, girls who are game enough to carry a bag of goods out of the stores and strong enough to barge people out of the way if they try to stop them, if you catch my drift.'

★

Bertha's eyes lit up at that. 'I could do that,' she said proudly, taking a large swig of her drink.

Right then, without being invited, the girl closest to me from the next table chipped in. 'We'd be interested, wouldn't we, Laura?'

The girl at her side, who was fairer and even more slightly built, but who had the same high cheekbones, nodded.

'Well, you two are right nosey parkers, ain't you?' I cut in, huffily.

But Kate stopped me in my tracks.

'Wait, Alice,' she said, laying her hand on my arm, and gazing at the pair of them, as if she were a horse dealer sizing up a couple of fillies. 'I reckon they'd come in handy. In fact, they might just be perfect. We need girls who can dress up to look nice, so they don't seem out of place in the stores.'

'Putting on the posh!' I laughed. She was right. Both of the girls were good-looking and with a few nice clothes, they'd pass for wealthy young ladies.

Bertha squinted at them for a moment.

'You're the Partridge girls, ain't you?' she said. 'Ain't it your mother Beryl who we always see pushing her pram full of whatever's fallen off the back of the costmonger's cart?'

The dark-haired girl shrugged, sulkily. 'That depends who's asking.'

'Our mum does what she can to make ends meet, but you can't hang her for it, can you?' said the fairer of the two.

The dark-haired girl chipped in, 'Me and my sister Laura here have seen enough jam to last a lifetime and hearing what that twerp Ernie did to Lily just makes us sick. We know a thing or two about stealing.'

Laura nudged her sister in the ribs. 'Madeline's been at it since she could crawl, nicking from the corner shop.'

Kate whispered in my ear, 'If their ma's a fence, she could be useful to help us sell the goods around the pubs and to the housewives, for a small fee. I reckon if we don't get her girls on board with us, we might have competition from them.'

I trusted Kate's judgement. She was better at hoisting than me and she'd even created those ridiculous bloomers to hide our loot. And there was strength in numbers. With six of us, we could run two teams of three, covering more shops in a day. We could be all over London, not just Selfridges and Gamages up in the West End, but by hopping on a tram, to Whitley's in Bayswater or Derry and Tom's in Kensington, plus all the jewellery shops and furriers down Bond Street.

I was beginning to feel excited about our new life, as thieves.

'Why don't you come and join us?' I said warmly, shifting my chair around to make space for them. 'I'm Alice and this is Kate, Gert and Bertha. Welcome to the gang.'

CHAPTER 11

MARY

Seven Dials, February 1900

The bitter cold of January gave way to icy February winds, which blasted through the streets of London, covering everything and every poor sod who slept rough with a hard frost.

The milk froze in the churns on the dairy cart and the undertakers were kept busy with paupers' funerals for the scraps of humanity who toiled in the workhouse on Endell Street. Gruel and hard labour made good bedfellows for the Grim Reaper that winter. At the laundry, my sisters' fingers were red-raw and cracked from the washing, but me and my girls in the Forty Thieves were cosy in leather gloves, fur-lined boots and high collars, perfecting our skills in the department stores of the West End.

I wore my diamond ring with pride, and it gave me an entry into the jewellery shops of Bond Street, as it was a very fine stone indeed. I'd make a great show of taking it off, enquiring about its quality and purity, pretending that I wanted to ask my fiancé to buy me another trinket. Trays of sparkling rings set with sapphires, rubies and emeralds were laid in front of me with great ceremony. Then, while Polly distracted the shop owner, I'd swap one of those beautiful bands for a worthless fake we'd picked up from one of the tallymen who sold their tat to hapless housewives around the Dials. It was a perfect little trick and very lucrative too.

Lord Harcourt and me became lovers after that first night of the Queen of Diamonds painting. He worked on the portrait for weeks on end and I felt so alive in his arms, and as he undressed me, gently unbuttoning the soft velvet gown, murmuring sweet nothings and nuzzling my neck, I knew I had captivated him too. But the thing which still thrilled me most was the diamond necklace, which I wore with such pride every time he painted me. I was weak and dizzy with longing as I gazed down at it and even as passion swept over me, it was the sparkle of the diamonds that sent a tingle of excitement all the way down to my toes.

And as for guilt for pinching another woman's husband, well, guilt is a funny thing, ain't it? Women are always riddled with it for one reason or another, especially if there's cheating involved. Oh, the hours I've spent listening to the housewives around the Dials whispering their little secrets and looking pained. All the worry about him indoors catching her at it, 'cos then she'd be in for a belting. Never mind that he was probably getting his leg over with some floozy at the same time as she was stealing a kiss from the tallyman, flirting with the milkman or dreaming of the handsome chimney sweep. Gossip spread like wildfire and the streets were always full of that kind of idle chatter. So, you might think I'd be feeling guilty about what I'd done with Lord Harcourt, but you'd be wrong.

Posh fellas in London have always had their wicked way with poor girls like me; it's an old story, as old as time itself. Would he have stopped if I'd asked him to? Perhaps, or perhaps not, but the fact was, I didn't want him to stop. And I didn't waste time suffering pangs of guilt because I didn't lead him astray, did I? The only deep lust I felt was for the diamonds and about that I had no regrets. Those diamonds, the diamonds he gave me to wear, *her* diamonds, had ignited a kind of longing in me. And, as Lord Harcourt had remarked, they were more at home on me, a slum girl, than on the woman who kept them safely tucked away in her jewellery box in Mayfair. Now, *that* gave me a secret pleasure. It glowed within me every time Lady Harcourt bossily told me to stand still or scolded me for not looking miserable and poverty-stricken enough for her stupid paintings.

When I went to his Piccadilly studio, the green velvet dress was always ready and waiting behind the modesty screen and then, tenderly, he'd kiss me and place the diamond necklace around my neck. As I stood there on the podium, swathed in emerald velvet, I lost myself in daydreams about the way they sparkled in the firelight, the feel of them against my skin, the weight of the biggest stone hanging down to my bosom, nestling there as if it had come home. And he noticed, mistakenly assuming that I was pining for him.

'Mary, I worry about the toll all this is taking on you and I can see you are suffering for it,' he said shamefacedly at the end of one evening, as I pulled on my coat and gloves. 'Is there anything I can do to make amends?'

I curtsied. 'Not at all, Your Lordship, it's just the cold weather making me look pinched. Please don't trouble yourself. I'll be more cheerful next time, I promise.'

'I'm so glad you feel that way,' he said, practically sighing with relief. 'Actually, I've finished the painting, so this will be the last of our sessions.' He unfolded a crisp pound note and handed it to me. 'The Queen of Diamonds is ready to meet her adoring public.' He ran his fingers through his mop of curls, smiling like a proud father.

'She'll be unveiled at the Royal Academy tomorrow night.'

I still had to keep my weekly appointments with Lady Dorothy Harcourt, who was planning on having an exhibition of her work, as well having a book printed of her paintings. Before I set off to see her, the diamond ring Lord Harcourt had gifted me was always hidden in a silk handkerchief at my hideout in the Seven Dials. I tucked it in an old tobacco tin behind a loose brick up the chimney. Much as I hated to be parted from it, I had a role to play for Lady Harcourt and it did not involve me strolling in with a massive sparkler on my finger.

Jem was in fine form that afternoon, muffled up against the cold, his cheeks like two rosy-red apples, clapping his hands together and singing as I towed him in his cart along Oxford Street and into Mayfair. The air was still freezing but the sun had broken through the clouds, and as I glanced up at the skies over London, I felt happier than I had in a long time. The struggles of my childhood seemed like a distant memory now; I was the Queen of Thieves, the leader of a fearless gang of hoisters, and we were living the high life on our ill-gotten gains.

The wind whistled through Grosvenor Square as I removed my fine leather gloves, tucking them safely into the pockets of my plainest overcoat. It wouldn't do for me to look too well-off, after all.

Maisie, the housemaid, was nowhere to be seen as I pushed open the door to the downstairs kitchen. The cook was huffing and puffing over some pie that hadn't risen as she'd hoped. I took off my boots and crept up the stairs to the hallway. The house was so quiet, you could have heard a pin drop. I put my finger to my lips to stop Jem from babbling in case Her Ladyship was sick with a headache again. We tiptoed up the grand staircase and were greeted by the sight of Miss White, stony-faced, glaring down at us.

'Her Ladyship needs to see you immediately!' she hissed, frog-marching me along the corridor as Jem struggled to keep up.

She rapped loudly on the door to the studio and pushed it open, shoving me inside. I swear, the temperature in that room was several degrees colder than the square outside, where the trees stood bare, and birds pecked in vain at the hard ground. Lady Harcourt was standing there, her hands folded in front of her, with a face like she was sucking a lemon. Her eyes, which I'd once thought were violet and full of kindness, had hardened, so they seemed almost frozen, and icy blue.

'Well,' she said accusingly, 'you've been busy, haven't you?'

I curtseyed, more out of confusion than politeness, because I wasn't late. 'Begging your pardon, Your Ladyship, I've been looking after my brother . . .'

Jem was hiding behind my legs, scared by her sharp tone. On the table she'd prepared a sewing basket with scraps of material and things to be mended. It was piecework, the mainstay of any woman's life around the Seven Dials, just to bring in a few pennies more. Yet here it was, in a mansion in Mayfair, ready to be used as a prop in another one of her paintings. I began to find the charade sickening.

'Have you nothing to say for yourself?' she went on, folding her arms across her chest, waiting for my reply.

That's when I caught sight of it, the huge canvas leaning against the far wall, covered with a sheet. I swallowed hard and felt the floor giving way beneath me. I knew what was behind it, but I didn't dare breathe a word.

'No, Your Ladyship.' How could I even begin to explain? What had Lord Harcourt told her? My heart was beating ten to the dozen as she stalked angrily across the room and swept the sheet from the picture. I gasped, as in the daylight, with the sun streaming through the big bay window, it was even more stunning than I recalled.

'You've been posing for my husband in secret, you ungrateful little wretch!' she cried. 'You have betrayed me! How dare you go behind my back, after everything I have done for you! I have never been so humiliated in all my life. Imagine how it felt for me to be in front of all our friends and half the Royal Academy for the great unveiling of my husband's latest work.

'And then to find you staring out at me,' she paused for breath, 'wearing *my* diamonds!'

She rushed at me, her face just inches from mine, her nostrils flaring, and grabbed me by the wrists so hard, that her nails dug into my flesh, drawing blood.

'You will tell me everything!' she screamed. 'What have you been getting up to with my husband? Tell me the truth!'

At that moment, I heard footsteps running down the corridor and the door burst open. Lord Harcourt stood in his shirtsleeves, his face contorting with worry and – there was no mistaking it – guilt.

'Dorothy, please!' he implored. 'I've explained everything to you. I painted her from memory, after the day you had a headache, and she came here to sit for you. Let her go, my darling, please don't upset yourself any further.'

Jem started to blub, with big, salty tears running down his rosy cheeks. He scampered to the table and hid underneath it, just as he did at home when my ma was screeching at us. I started to go to him, to offer him some comfort, but

Lady Harcourt kept a tight hold of me. And watching it all from the corner, with a look of utter delight on her face, was that evil housekeeper, Miss White. She was relishing every moment of this drama, which I knew full well would be played out later to all the servants below stairs.

Lady Harcourt loosened her grip as her husband rushed to her side, gathering her in his arms, soothing her, lulling her with sweet nothings. 'Don't upset yourself, my darling. Forgive me, forgive me, my love, my angel, she means nothing to me. It was just a portrait to show you how clever and wonderful you are, to pluck a nobody from the slums, to spot her beauty.'

'Beauty? Beauty?' she screeched, pushing him away. 'She's plain and poor and simple, without merit at all. How dare you paint her in my diamonds and, in the name of God, my slippers!'

She turned to look at me, but I was drawn to the portrait, captivated once more by the diamond necklace, shimmering, glinting at me. The truth was in that painting, in the brilliance of the diamonds, the knowing look of the girl in the green dress. A smile began to play upon my lips, and then, out of nowhere, I started to laugh. There was no need for me to say or do anything more. The diamond necklace was hers in name only, I was the true Queen of Diamonds and there was nothing she could do about it. She owned the stones, but those diamonds had chosen me and so, in fact, had her husband.

Her mouth opened and closed in disbelief.

'Oh, you little bitch!' she screeched. In an instant, she had picked up a pair of scissors from the workbasket on the table and ran, shrieking, towards the canvas, flailing her arms wildly. She plunged the scissors deep into the portrait before yanking downwards, hard. A horrible ripping sound filled the room. She turned to me, her eyes blazing with anger. 'See? You are nothing! I can destroy you!'

Then she plunged the scissors in again, this time aiming for the face of the Queen of Diamonds, who gazed on, as she was torn apart, her green velvet dress shredded, the canvas left hanging in tatters. When she had done her worst, Lady Harcourt lay down on the floor, sobbing like a child. Then, she looked up at her husband, her whole body wracked with great sobs, gasping, 'Did you touch her, Wilberforce? Did she throw herself at you, like the whore that she is?'

'No, no, my love,' he replied sheepishly. 'She's a mere slum girl, a nobody . . . surely you trust me? It was an artistic project, it was supposed to accompany your work, to show the world how clever you are. She's merely got above her station, as you can see by the way she laughed at your distress.'

'You have overshadowed my achievements, my art,' she wept, hurling herself on the carpet again.

He glanced momentarily at the beautiful work she had destroyed with her rage, but made a decision, there and then, to do whatever he needed to do to save his marriage. 'But everyone shall see what you have created, your paintings, your drawings, how wonderful you are! We shall hold your exhibition and publish your book for the whole of London, for the whole world to see, I promise you. People will flock to see your work and gaze in wonder at what you have created.'

He shot me a look that begged me not to expose him as a liar, by telling the truth about the sittings at his studio in Piccadilly, never mind what we had got up to together. I had no intention of spilling the beans because who would believe his word over mine anyway? He had wealth and power, and as he said, I was just a nobody from the slums.

My main concern was Jem, who was so terrified that he'd wet himself. The poor little mite was sitting in a puddle under the table. I ran to him, scooping him into my arms. I didn't see much of anything else because Miss White grabbed me by the scruff of my neck and marched me out of the room down the stairs and – for once in my life – out of the front door of that grand mansion at 7 Grosvenor Square, before slamming it firmly shut behind me.

I hurried home to the Seven Dials, stopping only to cradle Jem from time to time and soothe his sobbing. I never thought I'd be relieved to see the thin palls of smoke rising from the chimney stacks of my slum, but it was the sweetest sight that afternoon because it meant we were finally home, away from Mayfair and Lady Harcourt and her rage.

But as I made my way up the narrow, cobbled lanes towards my tenement, the street was eerily quiet. No urchins were playing chase or swinging off the lampposts and the only sound was the wind whistling through the alleyway.

I stopped outside our door, with its peeling paint and rotten wood, leaning against it to shove it open. Ma was standing there in the scullery, her hands on her hips, and Ada was with her, with a look on her face that was sheer delight. For beside them both, with his thumbs tucked into a thick leather belt around his middle, was a cozzer. His blue-bottle helmet was perched on the table, as if he'd made himself right at home, and beside it was Ma's best teapot and three steaming mugs of tea. It was a sickening sight.

I froze for an instant, before forcing a smile.

'This is a funny get-together, ain't it?' I said, stepping towards them, as if I hadn't a care in the world. My heart was beating like a drum, but I knew better than to give myself away. Jem toddled towards Ma, pulling at her apron. She brushed him off and he sat down on the floor at her feet.

'Mary Carr,' said the cozzer, breaking into a wide grin. 'I've heard so much about you, and now here you are, in the flesh, so to speak.'

Ma looked at the floor in shame, but Ada glared at me, with such a look of triumph, it took all my strength not to walk up to her and slap her stupid little face.

'That's me,' I said. 'But I shouldn't listen to idle gossip if I were you, Constable.' I began to unbutton my coat, pulling off my gloves, 'The Dials is full of liars and thieves, ain't that what they say?'

He laughed at that.

'And I hear you are the biggest thief of them all, my girl,' he boomed. 'And having received some very interesting information about you and your gang of late, I'm going to have to ask you to come down to the station to answer some questions.'

If looks could kill, I swear Ada would have dropped down dead on the spot right then. I stopped glaring at her and shrugged my shoulders at him.

'I think you'll find you're wasting your time, Constable, just like all the cozzers who ever set foot on this manor. Nobody will say a word about me because there ain't nothing to say. I'm as honest as the day is long. Ain't that right, Ma?'

She shuffled her feet and stared at the cracked red quarry tiles of the scullery floor. There was no need to ask Ada to vouch for me because I knew by then she'd grassed me up, the evil cow. My own family had turned their backs on me, the cowards, after everything I'd done for them.

The cozzer moved towards me, clasping a pair of handcuffs.

'Are you going to come quietly, or will you make a fuss like your friend, Polly?'

That winded me and I gasped.

My mouth went dry. 'You leave her alone! She's nothing to do with any of it.'

'She was picked up stealing from Selfridges earlier and she's in a cell singing like a canary the last I heard,' said the cozzer, putting his face so close to mine I could see the five o'clock shadow on his chin. 'So the game's up, Mary.'

He grabbed hold of me and roughly clapped the handcuffs on me, before pulling me through the door and into the street. A few people came out to watch as he dragged me away over the cobbles.

But the saddest thing was that as I was taken from the Seven Dials, Jem started to cry for me, shouting my name, over and over, until his sweet little voice was so far away that I couldn't hear him anymore.

CHAPTER 12

MARY

Bow Street, February 1900

It's the gloom that hits you first, then the hardness of the plank of wood that passes for a bed in the police cells. But the worst thing that night was hearing Polly sobbing and knowing I could do nothing to help her.

Oh, they roughed her up good and proper by the sound of it, until she was screaming at them to stop. I heard his laugh, that booming sound, echoing off the stone walls, and I knew then that cozzer who'd arrested me was one of the thugs beating the living daylights out of her and enjoying every minute of it too. I cupped my hand to my ear and pressed it to the dank wall, to hear what he was saying. All I could catch were muffled snatches of conversation before her piercing screams started again.

'Just tell me who . . .'

'Is Mary the Queen of Thieves?'

Then Polly would shout, 'No! No! I ain't saying nuffink, so help me God!'

That was a big mistake, his putting us in cells next to each other, because as dawn broke, I realised that the law had nothing on me other than what my sister, Ada, and Ma had told them. So, I resolved to keep my mouth shut, come what may, and to get even with those who'd betrayed me. Polly and me had agreed at the start that we'd never

ever grass each other up. And, God love her, she'd been true to her word. The thing is, the cozzers could never break her because they didn't know what her life was like before. We had something together in our gang, the Forty Thieves – a sense of belonging, of real family. And no amount of prison hardship would ever change that.

After a meagre breakfast of watery tea and a lump of stale bread, the door to my cell was opened and I was hauled roughly to my feet by that smug, big thug. Polly shuffled out of her cell next door looking like a broken doll, with her face covered in bruises and two black eyes. She glanced up at me, and managed a smile, before she was shoved down the corridor by a reed-thin policeman, who took great delight in making her suffer by aiming punches at her ribs as she walked along.

'Chin up, Polly,' I whispered. 'I promise I'll sort this out somehow.'

She turned and flashed me her gap-toothed grin and I knew then, whatever they did, they'd never break her.

The big cozzer got his hands on me, roughing me up as I was marched along the corridor behind her. 'No talking to the other prisoner!'

'We'll see what the magistrate has to say about the pair of you but until then, not another word,' he huffed, as we climbed the stairs. I rolled my eyes at him, and he gave me a thick ear for my trouble. That stung like hell, but it was worth it just to wind him up.

The Black Maria was waiting outside, with its glossy horses chomping at the bit to be on their way, ferrying us to the courthouse. A small crowd had gathered and there were a few whistles and jeers as we clambered inside, our hands cuffed, and the door clanged shut. That big lump sat between us in the back, spreading his legs, so that we had to perch at either end of the thin bench, as the caged cart rolled its way over the cobbles, with London just visible through the bars on the windows. Poor Polly winced with every lump and bump in the road; she was beaten black and blue and there was barely a picking on her to provide any padding.

'You've been a plague on the West End these past months,' the cozzer said icily, as we approached the court. 'And now, Mary Carr, you and your accomplice will face justice.'

I'd never seen the inside of a court room before, although I'd heard of judges in scarlet robes, and rooms adorned with fine wood panelling, and everyone talking in hushed tones. It's fair to say that on any other occasion, I might have been quite impressed by it all, but my head was spinning.

We were hurried through a side entrance, down some stone steps and along a corridor so narrow that the cozzer's broad shoulders practically touched the sides. Then it was up some more steps and into the dock, where the cozzer took up his position at the end of the bench, puffing his chest out as if he'd arrested some arch criminals who'd stolen the Crown Jewels rather than a couple of slum girls who'd had some fun feathering their nests.

The clerk and ushers were already having a hard time keeping order as word of our arrest had got around and nobody from the Seven Dials wanted to miss the excitement of one of their own being up before the beak. The public gallery was packed to the rafters and some of the old grannies had even brought their knitting and piecework along with them. Say what you like about the Dials, but the folk from round that way did love a spectacle. I just wasn't too keen on being part of it.

I glanced around the room but was disappointed to see that not one member of the Forty Thieves had come to show their support. Polly read my mind and murmured, 'They hightailed it off to the East End at the first sign of trouble, Mary.' That sat badly in my gut, or perhaps it was just the stale loaf giving me indigestion.

'The court will rise!' croaked the clerk, who was suffering a bad cold and kept pulling out the most enormous hand-kerchief, as big as a ship's sail, to blow his nose.

The judge strode in, wearing his long white horsehair wig and red gown.

The prosecution, a balding bloke with a paunch, leapt to his feet, tucking his thumbs into his waistcoat as he began to outline the case against Polly. The whole proceedings reminded me of a Punch and Judy show I'd seen as a nipper. Polly had been caught red-handed in Selfridges with a couple of pairs of stockings and a silk blouse tucked into a secret pocket under her skirt. I had to stop myself from yelling, 'Oh no she wasn't!'

The judge eyed her, resting his jowly chin in his hands as he lapped up every detail of her crimes. But then, just as the prosecution was about to park his considerable backside on the wooden bench, the judge raised an eyebrow and said, 'And what evidence do you have in relation to this other young lady I have here before me, this Mary Carr?'

I stood up to speak, to protest my innocence, but that cozzer grabbed hold of me and pulled me back into my seat.

'She is the leader of this gang of crafty and devious shoplifters, known as the Forty Thieves, Your Honour,' said the prosecution, flicking his gown as he gesticulated in my direction. 'She hails from the slums of the Seven Dials and has become known locally as the Queen of Thieves, such is her talent for stealing.'

The judge stifled a yawn. 'Yes, yes, but what evidence do you have of her involvement?'

'Certain information passed to the police from reliable sources, who have until now, been afraid to speak out,' said the prosecution with great flourish, like a magician showing off his best trick. That didn't impress the judge one bit. He banged his gavel, making the poor clerk jump about six feet in the air.

'I cannot convict a girl on hearsay! Where is the evidence? Have you recovered items she has stolen?'

The prosecution looked desperately at the cozzer next to me, who was fumbling with his fingers, going redder and redder.

I smirked.

'No, Your Honour,' said the lawyer. 'I was told the evidence was very reliable and the police have for some time known that Mary Carr is the head of the ring of thieves but have been unable to find anyone to swear to it until now.'

'And who is the witness?'

'Her sister, Your Honour.'

The judge shook his head and muttered, 'Sister indeed!'

'Stand up, Miss Carr,' he said. 'I will hear from you. What have you to say for yourself?'

'If it may please the court, it was my sister who told the police stories about me,' I began, simpering in my poshest accent, inwardly thanking God for the time I'd spent learning to copy Lady Dorothy Harcourt's voice. 'She is jealous that I have been working this past year as an artist's model for a fine lady up in Mayfair. Through this endeavour of my own, I have been lucky enough to earn more than my sister does down at the laundry.'

That piqued his interest.

'I see,' he said. 'An artist's model you say? And you are not involved in this ring of thieves, this scourge of the West End shops?'

'No, Your Honour,' I said contritely, 'I swear I know nothing about it. It's just idle gossip around the slums against a girl who has tried to make good on an honest path. You must forgive my sister, she's always made stories, ever since we were young, and our father abandoned our mother. It's her way of making her life better than it really is, as she has to work in the laundry, day after day, you see.'

Polly, God love her, stifled a giggle at the sheer brass neck of what I was saying.

'Very well,' said the judge. 'I must remind officers of the law not to waste my time bringing people into this court based on nothing more than silly girls' gossip! Queen of Thieves, indeed! You are free to go from this court.'

His eyes narrowed as he went on. 'But as for you, Miss Polly McGuinness, there will be no such leniency. I find you guilty of three counts of theft and sentence you to twelve months in Holloway Prison. I hand down this sentence to make clear to all of London that such thievery will not be tolerated!'

There was a gasp in the court at that. He banged his gavel again and a hush fell over the room. I wanted to jump for joy because I was free, but the look on Polly's battered face as she was dragged away down the stairs to face her sentence in jail weighed on me like a ton of bricks.

I wandered back to the Seven Dials in a daze, weak with shock from the loss of my deputy, Polly, and the sleepless night I'd spent in the cells, not to mention the betrayal by own flesh and blood.

My mind was racing. I wanted to get even with Ada, but I needed my gang around me, and they were nowhere to be seen. Instead of the welcoming smiles and hugs from people who'd been so keen to buy my stolen wares in the past, I got nothing more than the cold shoulder and the sound of doors hurriedly slamming as kids were pulled indoors. Oh, they were a two-faced bunch, the Cockneys. They'd come and see me in the dock, to gloat at my misfortune, but now I was down on my luck, my own community had turned its back on me, that much was clear.

To top it off, a few of the costergirls started catcalling to me from the safety of their boyfriends' fruit and veg barrows. In the past, they'd cosied up to me, with their moth-eaten velvet jackets and their split boot leather, offering me a mug of gin or a tot of rum in return for my finest silk stockings or a nice ostrich feather for their hats. Now, they delighted in tormenting me.

'You ain't looking so clever, Mary Carr!'

'Lost your gang, have you? Feeling lonesome? You snooty cow!'

As I scurried down Long Acre, with my head low, I couldn't help hearing the cry of the newspaper seller, touting the evening edition of the *London Evening News*: 'Read all abaht it! Forty Thieves gang broken up! Scourge of shopkeepers jailed, but gang leader walks free!' I could have sworn the whole street was watching me as I dashed along, desperate to reach the safety of my hideout.

A crow screeched on the timbers overhead as I pushed my way into the derelict house. Wasting no time, I ran to the fireplace and put my hand up the chimney, scrabbling for the tobacco tin in my hiding place. A sense of relief swept over me as I pulled it out and the diamond gleamed at me in the half-light. With that ring on my finger, I was somebody again. I felt the power of that jewel coursing through my veins, and it gave me the strength to carry on. Next, I pulled up the floorboards, taking out bundles of my best dresses, as well as a carpet bag filled with trinkets, stockings and silk handkerchiefs. That lot was worth a pretty penny, I can tell you.

As I changed into my finest clothes and gathered all the things I'd stolen, the cold, hard truth of my situation began to sink in. I couldn't stay in the Dials because it would only be a matter of time before someone betrayed me again. There was no way on God's green earth I wanted to end up in the nick again with that policeman, or in front of that judge for that matter.

As I emerged from the alleyway, my mind was made up. Whatever my future held, I had enough saved up to start afresh in the East End, with the rest of the girls, once I'd tracked them down. What's more, I was skilled enough as a seamstress to get an honest job until I could get the gang back together. That would help keep my head above water. It was only a matter of time, because in a year, Polly would be free, and we could make a go of things again.

I marched across the cobbles with my bulging carpet bag, heading towards my old front door. I pushed it open, purposefully, because my mind was made up and I was in no mood for an argument.

I was leaving the Seven Dials and I was taking Jem with me.

Ma was slumped at the scullery table, with a pile of money in front of her, next to a row of gin bottles, some of them half empty. Ada was stirring a pot on the range, humming to herself as if she hadn't a care in the world. She went white as a sheet when she caught sight of me, though.

'I've got a bone to pick with you,' I said, moving towards her.

She grabbed a knife from the sideboard. I can't say I was scared, as it was so blunt it would barely go through butter.

'You cowardly bitch, grassing me up to the law,' I spat.

'Oh, spare me!' she shouted back, brandishing the knife in my direction. 'You had it coming, you and your stupid little gang of idiot girl thieves! You were bound to get caught sooner or later, so you can't lay that at my door. Polly got herself collared and it was no surprise when they came asking questions about you! I had to tell 'em something or they'd have turned the house upside down. You saw the size of that cozzer. He was built like a brick shithouse.'

'That's no excuse for what you did, Ada, and you know it,' I said. 'Grassing up your own flesh and blood.'

I turned to my mother, who was gazing up at me, glassy-eyed with booze.

'And you!' I said. 'Betraying your own daughter to the cozzers! Have you no shame after everything I've done for you?' I picked up a fistful of cash and threw it in her face. 'Is that what they paid you for the tip-off?'

'Nah,' she slurred. 'That was the posh lady, that was. Very generous, too.'

A sheaf of papers lay on the table in front of her. She picked them up and waved them under my nose. 'I signed them, see?'

My blood ran cold. Ada's mocking laugh was ringing in my ears.

'Signed what?' I said, seizing the papers from her. It was all there in bold black lettering:

Adoption Order: *Gentlemen, it is hereby agreed that the said child Jeremy Carr, of Earlham Street, Seven*

Dials in the Parish of St Giles, born in the year of Our Lord 1888, is hereby declared the legal son of Lord and Lady Wilberforce Harcourt, residing at 7 Grosvenor Square, Mayfair, London, W1.

Margaret Carr, mother, of the aforementioned address, declares there is no legal impediment to her becoming a signatory to this agreement and she willingly enters into it, for the good of her son, who will be raised by Lord and Lady Harcourt as their own.

I crumpled, my legs giving way, as I sank to the floor. 'What in the name of God have you gone and done, Ma?'

'Oh, don't be like that,' she crowed. 'That posh couple and their butler came around the night you got arrested and they had a right bee in their bonnet about wanting to help us out by offering Jem a good life, a posh life up in Mayfair. Seems like you made quite a big impression on Her Ladyship with all your modelling sessions, so you did, and she developed quite a soft spot for our Jem. The poor lady confessed she'd lost a baby boy in childbirth and meeting our Jem made her realise what she's been missing all these years. His Lordship was very keen to have a son, because, as he told me, only a male child will fulfil Her Ladyship's needs as a mother. Oh, we had quite the chat did me and His Lordship! There's no side to him is there? He didn't come over all hoity-toity with me. So, I was happy to oblige.'

The whole room was spinning as she went on. 'Now, you're a dark horse ain't you? You never told me you were posing for paintings. Hope you kept your clothes on!' She slapped her thigh and shrieked with laughter at her own pathetic joke.

My mouth had gone dry, and the blood was rushing in my ears.

'But you didn't give Jem away, Ma. Sweet Jesus, tell me you didn't do that?'

Ada put her hands on her hips. 'Well, what else was she to do, Mary? You were in the clink, and our ma has enough worries on her plate! A posh family came along offering Jem a better life, better than anything you could provide from Holloway Prison for all we knew. Why should you be the only one to benefit from their kindness? I've got my hands full at the laundry. Jem's going to be a young gentleman. You should be happy for him. Stop being so bleeding selfish, Mary.'

'That's right,' said Ma, standing up unsteadily and raising a bottle of gin in a toast. 'We're celebrating Jem's good fortune. Cheers!'

'No!' I cried, clamping my hand to my mouth in disbelief. 'You can't have done it! You can't!' Tears filled my eyes as I ran to the bedroom. 'Lady Harcourt's an evil cow. She'll make his life a living hell, just to punish me.'

'Punish you?' squawked Ma. 'For what? Ooh, don't tell me you got your leg over with her hubby, you sly little mare!'

Ada shrieked with laughter at that, tears of hilarity rolling down her cheeks. 'I bet you did, posing as an artist's model, my arse! You're just a common floozy.'

The cot I'd bought him, with its goose-down quilt and soft pillow, was bare. Jem was nowhere to be seen, sold by his own mother to a woman who wanted to spite me for being Queen of Diamonds.

And there was nothing I could do to stop it.

The London Evening News

5th December 1923

BOB-HAIRED BANDIT AND 'BABYFACED' ACCOMPLICE IN £500 FURS HAUL!

By Walter Pritchard, Crime Correspondent

Shopkeepers from Bond Street are counting the cost of another daring raid by a gang of female thieves and their brazen leader, who police are calling the 'Bob-Haired Bandit'.

Fur coats, wraps and collars worth several hundred pounds were stolen in the latest outrage, which took place in broad daylight in one of London's busiest shopping thoroughfares.

Police say they are determined to apprehend the gang, which appears to be frequenting shops all over the city, targeting luxury items. The light-fingered ladies, who shop managers say are polite and very well-dressed, use a combination of distraction and trickery to carry out their criminal missions. Witnesses say the leader is a striking, tall young woman, who usually wears a stylish hat over her bobbed coiffure, and speaks very little, other than to express an interest in viewing and trying on the most expensive items in the shop. Her accomplice, who is small and has an almost childlike innocence about her, is a wily and determined thief, who apparently makes silks and furs disappear from shelves and counters, as if by magic. Staff believe items are speedily and carefully concealed under clothing or stuffed into bags which are then passed on to other gang members lurking nearby. But such is the skill of the Bob-Haired Bandit and her mob that nobody has been caught.

It raises the prospect of a highly organised female criminal gang wreaking havoc in London's top stores, at a time when Mayfair is reeling from a spate of house burglaries, in which diamonds and gems worth thousands have been stolen. The thief is believed to be a burglar who enters the homes of wealthy families while they sleep. Debutantes all over London are living fear of the villain, who is nicknamed Jack the Cat, because he is so stealthy.

Charles Vimpany, owner of Vimpany's Furriers on Bond Street, victim of the latest theft of furs by the female gang, said, 'These very plausible young ladies spent a considerable amount of time trying on and praising my sable coats and accessories. One even said her own coat needed mending to distract me. She was well-dressed, tall, and quite striking to look at, with her hair in a fashionable short 'bob' cut. I told her I was happy to repair the item, but you can imagine my horror when she and her friend hurried off and I then discovered that the coats they had tried on in the changing room were no longer anywhere to be found.

'On closer inspection, I realised that several fur collars, as well as fox fur cuffs and an ermine wrap, had also disappeared from my counters. It was a terrible loss of stock worth over £500, as some of my furs had come from Parisian fashion designers in the latest styles. I hope the police catch these dangerous women. One of them even laughed and bade me "Cheerio!" as she left my shop, which I find shocking.'

Chief Inspector John Wright, of Scotland Yard, said more would be done to catch the culprits. 'This is a disturbing trend and one which the police will clamp down on. These women may think they are going to get away with it, but we are redoubling our efforts to catch them.'

CHAPTER 13

ALICE

Elephant and Castle, December 1923

'Ain't that an absolute beauty?'

Kate gazed longingly at the full-length chinchilla coat, in white, soft grey and black, which took pride of place in the window of Le Grand's Bond Street shop window.

It was the furs we loved the best, not just for selling on but to wear, because they made us feel so damn glamorous. And it was fair to say that Kate loved them the most.

The softness of a sable, the sheer delight of swathing herself in an ermine wrap or putting her little feet into fur-lined boots, brought a kind of glow to her. It made her stylish and with every hoisting trip, more agile and daring. But that chinchilla coat was something special and I knew from the moment she laid eyes on it that she was going to pinch it.

We were stealing from the finest stores at least three times a week on our shopping expeditions and I'd noticed her taking bigger risks. She just couldn't help herself. I'm not going to claim I was unhappy about it because our little enterprise had changed all our lives for the better, but nobody wanted to get caught.

'How on earth do you think you're going to swipe that from the window display without being collared, Babyface?' I laughed, pulling her away from that shop, and off towards

Selfridges, where we could fill our pockets with stockings, scarves, belts and easy pickings from the jewellery counter. I was teasing her by calling her the nickname the newspapers had given her after our daring exploits made headline news. But it was affectionate too, because we all called her Babyface now, more than Kate. I was the Bob-Haired Bandit, and she was my sweet accomplice with babyish good looks.

But, despite my concerns, she wouldn't be deterred.

The next morning, we set off for Bond Street again, but this time, she produced a pillow from her carpet bag.

'That's for you to shove up your dress, Alice,' she giggled. 'You might even find pregnancy suits you.'

I rolled my eyes. It sounded like a strange plan to me but deep down, I trusted her judgement, although I was beginning to wonder if she'd gone too far this time. The Partridges burst out laughing when they saw me in the street looking like I was up the duff, creasing over, with tears rolling down their faces.

'I know, I know,' I said, 'I look six months' gone!'

Gert and Bertha were just as bad, teasing me about who the father was, on the bus we took over the bridge to get to the West End.

'You may laugh now,' said Babyface, swivelling round in her seat and pouting at them, 'but it's all part of my brilliant plan, you'll see.'

I was dizzy with the thrill of going hoisting with her, of marching into shops looking like we owned the place. We were more than a team, we seemed to anticipate each other's next move, signalling it with a raised eyebrow or a look. The other girls were caught up in it too, sparkling with the thrill of what the day's thieving would bring.

We'd developed a method, a crafty one, of rolling the furs, still on the hanger, and shoving them down the leg of our hoisters drawers while staff were getting something from the storeroom or serving another 'customer' who was very demanding. The willowy Partridge girls were always a part of our ruses, taking great delight in being as rude and difficult as possible to buy us valuable time, posing as wealthy, bored young ladies.

Oh my word, we had such a hoot learning how to roll and clout those furs down our drawers because they were bulky and it wasn't easy to get them small enough, but we were determined. We spent hours at it at home, rolling and unrolling, shoving them down the waistbands of our skirts and into our bloomers until we could do it in the blink of an eye.

It became our secret, our special trick, because I could get one down each leg and a wrap or fur collar under my gusset and still walk out of Gamages or Selfridges as if I hadn't a care in the world. I was proud of that because I was the best at it.

But today was different because Babyface was not intending to shove that coat down her knickers. She was going to walk out of that shop in broad daylight wearing it.

And the flutter I felt as we headed to the shops was not excitement, but nerves.

As we walked into the furriers, Babyface produced a gold ring we'd nicked from Gamages, so that I could pretend to be married, in my pregnant state, to avoid suspicion. The shop was quiet as the grave, so I wasn't holding out too much hope that her plan would work, but she took off her fox fur coat, laid it on the counter, and began telling the shopkeeper a tall story about needing to have it re-modelled.

'I want the latest look,' she said. 'I think it's rather old-fashioned, don't you?'

He was a jolly man, plump, with his glasses on a brass chain around his neck and a pinstripe waistcoat in a fine, navy cloth. He popped the spectacles on the end of his round nose and peered at the fur, running his fingers over the lining to work out how it could be altered. Just then, the shop door was pushed open, and the Partridges sashayed in, talking loudly to each other.

Madeline pulled off her leather gloves, which she'd deliberately torn a hole in, plonking them on top of the fur coat.

'Is there any chance you could find me a replacement for these gloves, please? I feel such a mess wearing them, it's quite shocking.'

'Certainly, Miss, but I'm just serving this other young lady,' he began politely. 'I won't keep you a moment.'

'But we're in a dreadful hurry!' gasped Laura, as if her life depended on it. 'We simply must get to Liberty or Aunty Annie will be cross with us.'

'That's all right,' said Babyface, simpering at the shopkeeper. 'I don't mind if you serve them first.'

That was my cue. I clasped my hand to my head, and started to groan, 'Oh, I feel so giddy, the room is going black . . .'

'Help her!' shrieked Babyface. 'She's going to fall and she's with child!'

I let my knees crumple under me, as I shut my eyes, slumping to the ground, clasping the pillow in case it slipped out. Madeline let out a cry of horror. Out of the corner of my eye, I spied Bertha and Gert hanging around outside the shop, in case they were needed to block the entrance to stop any other customers from entering at the crucial moment in our scheme.

The shopkeeper was quite large, but he was light on his feet, and he was at my side in an instant, gathering me into his arms, like a true gentleman, 'Oh, you poor dear lady, are you quite all right?'

'Water,' I croaked. 'I think I need a glass of water, it's the baby, making me feel sick.'

'Do you think I should call for a doctor?' said Babyface, as the shopkeeper sprung to his feet and rushed to the back of the shop to get me a drink. It only took a split second for her to yank the chinchilla coat from the mannequin in the window and slip her arms into it, shooting me a wicked grin. Then she snatched her fox fur and flung it over the top.

She was out of the shop in a trice, with me at her heels, running quite fast for someone who was so far gone, it had to be said. That raised a few eyebrows in Bond Street. Gert and Bertha strolled away in the other direction, while Madeline and Laura hung around until the shopkeeper clocked that his prize fur had gone walkabout, before making their excuses and hurrying off to meet their fake aunt in Liberty.

Despite my fears that Babyface might have pushed things too far, it was the perfect hoist.

We'd already made a few headlines with our sprees and after our latest escapade, there would surely be more. That brought us a kind of notoriety down the pub. Babyface didn't seem to mind; in fact, she liked it because it made her feel famous, special even. We were invincible, riding high, the toast of the boozer on a Friday night. Men admired us for our sheer brass neck and women were grateful for making their drab lives a bit more bearable.

I never regretted leaving the factory, not for one minute, although I did miss Lily and thought of her often. Tears for her couldn't change what had happened and as the months passed, I found my heart was heavy, but my eyes were dry whenever she crossed my mind.

Besides, running the hoisting business took up all my time. We had an endless supply of customers asking to buy our wares. Girls from the factories and the laundries, or the housewives eking out a thankless existence in the grim cobbled terraces nestling by the Thames.

Some of them could only afford a pair of stockings or a dress, but others badgered their hubbies to shell out for that one thing which would set them apart from other women down the pub – a fur coat. And don't think it was just the lowlifes who wanted our ill-gotten gains. Dear me, no! Even the doctor came sneaking around the pub with his leather bag, pretending he was looking for a patient, when he really wanted to put in an order for a fox fur coat for his good lady wife in time for Christmas! We started off rattling around with a few coins in our pockets from hoisting but by the end of a few months' hard graft, we had purses stuffed with cash.

We shared it fair and square between all of us, putting a bit extra by for Beryl, our fence, because she did wear out quite a lot of shoe leather pushing her pram around the cobbled streets of South London hawking our goods. It made the tallyman quite cross because we undercut him and the moneylenders weren't too pleased either, but they took one look at Gert and Bertha and thought better of saying anything to our faces about it. I carried my hatpin and a trusty razor in my handbag, just in case. Word had got round we'd given Ernie from the factory a good clump so that helped my reputation too, as a woman not to be messed with.

We moved out of Mrs Dally's and found ourselves better lodgings in a tenement, Queen's Buildings, down at the Elephant and Castle. She had started to get suspicious about the fact that we weren't bringing her pots of jam from Pink's anymore. It didn't take long for her to find out me and Babyface had been given our cards and Gert and Bertha had walked off the job too. Yet, here we were, always paying the rent on time, with plenty of money to spare too. I think at one point she feared we were on the game, like the brasses earning their living in the dark alleyways down by the river.

So, I think she was relieved when we packed our belongings and left.

But not everyone around our way was pleased with our success.

'Are you two swanning around the parish like ladies from Mayfair again?' said Pearlie, giving me and Babyface a hard stare as we made our way to the pub after our chinchilla hoist. Her dog, Geezer, gave an indignant bark at the pair of us, for good measure.

It was true that Babyface flaunted our wealth, all dolled up in her furs around the market, gazing at herself in shop windows and primping up her curls but it wasn't like that for me. I loved my sable coat because it did look good, but it also kept me warm, which was just sensible in freezing weather. Some kids were kicking a lump of ice about like a football and the fog was rolling in from the river, catching me at the back of my throat as we lingered by her flower stall.

'Oh, leave it out, Pearlie,' I said, breaking into a smile and offering her a crisp pound note from my purse. 'Stop being so bloody bitter and go and treat yourself to something nice up the market before they shut up shop.'

'It's your time I want, not your money, Alice,' she said, turning her nose up at my money. 'I explained that to

146

you before. When are you coming to see me again? I'm missing our little chats.'

Babyface made some unkind comment about Pearlie being mad as a hatter, so I waved her on to the pub to get the drinks in, while I took a moment to sit with Pearlie and keep her sweet.

Now, don't get me wrong, it wasn't that I cared about her that much, but her stories were entertaining, and Mary Carr's life had taken a downward turn, so I wanted to know how it ended for the Queen of Thieves, given that she was in my line of business.

'I'll come by tomorrow and we can spend all the morning chatting if you like,' I said. 'But I've got Babyface and the girls to think about too, surely you understand that? We've had a good week and there's plenty to celebrate. I thought you'd be happy for me . . .'

'You're the Queen of Thieves now, ain't you?' she said, with a note of sadness in her voice.

I shrugged. 'People probably call me all sorts behind my back but if they respect what I'm doing and it means I don't have to spend my days down that bleeding factory, who cares?'

'I care,' said Pearlie, under her breath, as I waved goodbye and headed off to the boozer.

The party was in full swing as I pushed open the doors to the pub. I was hit by the fug of ciggie smoke, a blast of heat from the coal fire glowing in the grate, and the songs of people in high spirits after a week at work. It was the smell of cold and poverty having a knees-up and warming its fingers by the fire, drowning its sorrows and searching for hope in the bottom of an empty pint glass. It didn't smell all clean and fancy, of flowers and perfumes, like the stores up West, but it was a scent I knew well. It was home to me.

Babyface and the girls were the centre of attention, dressed like stars from the stage or the silent films that were all the rage down at the picture house, in silk dresses which fell to the knee, with strings of pearls about their necks. The Partridge girls had feathers in their hair and even Bertha and Gert had put a bit of rouge on their cheeks and done their curls nicely. I was wearing a beautiful red felt cloche hat that I'd pinched from Gamages. It had a cream silk ribbon running around it and was adorned with a silk carnation in the same hue and I ain't ashamed to say, I didn't look half bad in it. I'd practically skipped out of the store when I nicked it. Underneath my sable, I was clad in a black velvet dress, with a square neckline, a dropped waist, and a collar of the finest lace. The whole outfit was set off by a row of stolen diamond rings which I'd snatched from a display cabinet in a jewellery shop in Oxford Street. Babyface had a matching set in emerald and very lovely they were too. In our furs and our finery, we stood out from the downtrodden housewives in their worn woollen coats and headscarves, quietly sipping at tiny glasses of sherry in the corner, watching us with a mixture of envy and amazement. I was feeling flush, so I opened my purse and bought the pub a round, which lightened the mood even further.

Some wag started playing 'Where Did You Get That Hat?' on the ivories, and before long the whole pub was joining in, 'Where did you get that tile, isn't it a nobby one, and just the proper style?', and crying with laughter when someone sang, 'She nicked it from Gamages, then ran a bleeding mile', in reply. The singing got more raucous as the drink kept flowing and soon the pub was packed to the rafters.

'I want to dance!' said Babyface, linking arms with me, 'Let's go up West, what do you say, Alice?'

I shuffled my feet self-consciously. My only memories of dancing were as a nipper in the Seven Dials, jigging about outside the theatres in the hope that one of the quality might dip their hand in their pocket and chuck me a penny for my efforts.

But before I could put her off, the Partridges had joined in. 'Let's go and have fun like the posh girls do, and drink champagne and twirl around the dancefloor.' And Bertha and Gert threw their weight behind the idea too, so before long, glasses were emptied. I found myself being propelled through the pub doors and back into the freezing cold night, trying to hail a hackney cab across the water, to the bright lights of clubland.

CHAPTER 14

ALICE

Soho, London, December 1923

The church bells of the West End chimed eleven as our taxi nudged its way through the narrow backstreets of Soho. When the theatre curtains fell and the pubs were closing their doors to drinkers, this was where everyone went to carry on the party. And what a party it was down at the High Life club.

A queue had already formed on the narrow staircase down into the basement, where a band was in full swing, belting out jazz, with the top notes of the trumpet and saxophone screeching through the doors. Babyface barged her way forward in her chinchilla coat, like she was a film star. Posh girls, who were born with a silver spoon in their mouth and wanted for nothing, made way for her, as if they knew they were outclassed. We followed along behind her, like little ships bobbing in the wake of an ocean liner, chattering away at the top of our voices, buoyed by drink.

Inside, the dance floor was already full of couples foxtrotting around at quite a pace. And the most amazing thing was, the whole floor was glass, illuminated by coloured light bulbs, so the effect was dazzling. The women were impossibly beautiful, with blunt fringes cut into their bobbed and shingled hair, which was adorned with jewels and feathers. Some shimmied in beaded gowns which were daringly short, falling to the knee. Men in the smartest evening dress of black tailcoat, white waistcoats and stiff collars led them, gliding effortlessly over the twinkling lights. This wasn't the boorish good fun of the pub; the ladies' laughter wasn't raucous here, it sparkled.

The walls were painted silver and gold and dotted around the edge of the room were tables covered in crisp, white cloths. We made a beeline for an empty one, just as one of those fellas in a tailcoat darted across and pulled out a chair for himself.

'Oh, excuse me, ladies,' he said. 'It's so crowded in here, do you mind if I join you?'

The others started to giggle a bit when he chose the chair nearest to me, but I shrugged, 'Suit yourself.'

'May I have the pleasure of knowing your name?'

Babyface cut in, brandishing her enormous emerald rings under his nose. 'I'm Norah *Emerald a*nd my friend here is Alice *Diamond*,' she said, suppressing a giggle. He raised an eyebrow at that, pulling a silver cigarette case from the top pocket of his jacket. He flipped it open and offered me one.

'Don't smoke,' I said, trying not to be too distracted by how good-looking he was. His hair was slicked back and he had an unlined face, with even, regular features, which spoke volumes about his privileged life. There was something mesmerising about the way his eyes sparkled, but that could have been the drink in me talking.

He offered the case around the table and Babyface reached over and took a ciggie, blushing beetroot. She wasn't a smoker, not that I knew of, but she leaned forward, pursing her red lips at him, as he struck a match and lit it for her.

She inhaled deeply, which brought on a coughing fit, and I clapped her on the back. I snatched it from her and stubbed it out in the glass ashtray before she made herself sick. 'Baby, don't be daft,' I scolded.

She scowled at me. 'It opens the airways, Alice. That's what the adverts say!' It was as if she wanted to impress him, like all the rail-thin girls sitting around idly blowing smoke rings.

A waitress appeared and before anyone knew what was happening, this chap had delved into his wallet and was ordering us a bottle of champagne, at thirty-five shillings. That was more than a week's wages for most blokes. I knew then he was minted, but I didn't want us girls to be bought and paid for by any man. It was a matter of pride for us to pay our way.

'That's very kind,' I said, brandishing my purse stuffed with money under his nose, my diamond rings sparkling, 'but we can buy our own drinks.'

He smiled, his lips just curling at the corners, as if he was enjoying teasing me, as I handed over my money to the waitress. 'How very modern you are! May I ask you to dance, or do you girls only do that together as well?'

Laura and Madeline tittered to each other at that, just as they were whisked off by a couple of gents, who pulled them into the throng and started twirling them around like spinning tops. Gert and Bertha were grinning at the trumpet and the trombone players, who kept blowing them kisses in between notes, like a couple of lovesick schoolboys.

'Well?' said Mr Handsome. 'Do you want to dance with me, or must I beg?'

This bloke was really beginning to get under my skin for reasons I couldn't quite fathom. I wasn't the world's greatest dancer – I could kick my legs up and down in the boozer once I'd had a few – but I'd never done the kind of moves these girls were pulling off with such ease, so I felt a bit flustered. I looked at him, finding myself drawn to his mischievous smile, and then said, 'Well, why not?'

Babyface shot me a look, which was a mixture of disbelief and envy, but I thought if I got up to dance, it would teach her a lesson for trying to impress a man she'd didn't know from Adam by making up silly names and embarrassing herself with that cigarette. The waitress chose that moment to arrive with a chilled bottle of champagne, sending the cork flying skywards before she poured it into glasses, bubbles frothing over.

I got up, smoothing down the folds of my velvet dress and Babyface picked up a glass of fizz and drank deeply, as if she'd been without water in the desert for a week. Then she knocked back another.

Handsome offered me his hand.

Before I knew what I was doing, I took it.

He was strong but gentle, putting an arm around me, easing us into a space on the crowded dance floor, before picking up the pace. I let him lead me, unable to avoid his gaze as I was six feet tall in my gladrags and heels. He leaned in, his cheek touching mine. I could feel just how clean-shaven he was, and my stomach flipped. I tried to stop it, but it was useless – I was as soft in his arms as butter left out in the sun.

To my astonishment, once I let him take me where he wanted me to go, the steps came easily. I felt the music coursing through my body, moving with his insistent rhythm, and by the time the song ended, I was flushed and a bit breathless, possibly because he'd been whispering compliments in my ear the whole time.

Babyface scowled at me by way of greeting as we returned to our table.

He put out his hand to her. 'Miss Emerald, I'm neglecting you. May I have the pleasure of this dance?'

Well, she was off like a rat up a drainpipe, leaping to her feet and almost jigging with delight at the prospect of getting a turn around the club with him. I smiled indulgently at his act of kindness. After all, he'd picked me first and Babyface was probably now so plastered she'd fall flat on her face.

But she didn't. He scooped her up, almost protectively, guiding her out on the dance floor with the same care and attention he'd lavished on me. She was gazing up at him with a look of rapt delight, as he quickstepped her into the fray, her tiny frame doll-like against his. The band leader began crooning, 'Where are you from, my blue-eyed baby? Where is your pa? Who is your ma?'

The whole club was giddy with champagne as more corks popped and cheers went up. Handsome and Babyface moved in time to the music near our table. And then they were lost in a sea of partygoers, emerging like the crest of a wave in a froth of feathers and silks, amid whirling couples. She passed by, the white of her teeth flashing, smiling triumphantly in my direction.

I felt a stab of jealousy. And it wasn't just because she was dancing with Handsome – it was actually the way he was looking at her which troubled me the most. I felt a hot flush rising up my neck and took a sip of my drink to calm myself down, smiling as if I hadn't a care in the world while the green-eyed monster dug its claws into my guts.

As the clock struck one, the band leader called for hush, and announced a prize for the best-dressed young lady in the High Life.

'With thanks to our donor, who just loves to see young women of London looking so pretty, we proudly offer twenty-five guineas prize money to the brightest lady in the room, who can impress us with her stylish attire!'

The Partridges and Babyface didn't need to be asked twice. They scampered off to the cloakroom to retrieve their furs, before marching out onto the illuminated dance floor, to stand cheek by jowl with half a dozen of the aristocracy's finest beauties. They were lithe and long-limbed, gazing archly at these interlopers jostling them for a place in the line-up, as if it was a queue at pie and mash stall.

In the end, it was Babyface, wrapped in that stunning chinchilla coat, who drew the biggest cheer from the crowd. She broke into a huge grin, shining like a sunbeam, twirling around, as a fella stepped forward with a camera and a flashbulb went off. The bandleader came over with her prize money and kissed her on the cheek, before raising his baton for the final dance of the night.

At the first note, there was a stampede of people back on to the dance-floor, where they started windmilling their arms and stepping forward and back, kicking their legs, and twisting their feet in the craziest moves I had ever seen. It was a wonder nobody got a black eye or put their back out.

'It's the Charleston!' said Bertha, guffawing with laughter, as she was dragged away to dance. Babyface was the centre of attention, with men vying to dance with her, and she kicked and pouted, as if she was born for a life on the West End stage.

Handsome stayed by my side, taking hold of my hand, admiring my rings.

'Diamonds live for moments such as these,' he said. 'So much nicer than keeping the family jewels in a dusty safe, don't you think?'

I wasn't sure what he was getting at, but my family had never given me tuppence. I snatched my hand away. 'All bought and paid for through my own hard work,' I replied.

'No offence,' he smoothed.

Someone had lifted Babyface onto their shoulders and she was being paraded around the club like a Madonna at the Italian processions up in Islington.

'I think it's time to take her home,' I said, but when I turned to say goodbye to him, he had disappeared. I kept glancing around as we were leaving, but Handsome was nowhere to be seen.

There were a few sore heads down at Queen's Buildings the next day and it was after lunchtime when we finally dragged ourselves into the scullery to make a reviving cup of tea. I took one look at Bertha's face, which had gone a funny shade of green, before announcing, 'Right, you lot! This calls for a fry-up.' The smell of eggs and bacon brought Babyface from her bed, rubbing sleep out of her eyes. She smiled to herself as she sat down.

'Well, you look like the cat that got the cream!' said Gert, pouring us all a nice brew.

'I'm on a promise with that nice bloke from last night,' she said, twirling a lock of her hair around her skinny fingers.

I jumped, as if I'd been scalded, nearly dropping the eggs I was sliding onto plates. 'What on earth are you talking about?'

'Ooh, watch out Babyface, she'll be inviting you out to fight for him on the cobbles next,' said Gert.

'I'd lay money on that,' said Bertha, who'd bet on anything with a pulse.

I flicked a tea towel at the lot of them. 'You'd better spill the beans because this bloke was whispering sweet nothings in my lughole all night too, so I reckon he might be having you on.'

She shook her head and gave me a self-satisfied smile. One that made me want to slap some sense into her. 'You're wrong about that,' she said, 'because he's invited me to tea at the Ritz this afternoon!'

She spent ages getting all dolled up, carefully applying lipstick and powder and plumping up her curls, admiring her reflection in the mirror, before selecting a beautiful, knitted dress from a pile of our hoisted stuff. She was heading down the hall when I stepped out of my bedroom, with my coat and hat on.

'Oh, for gawd's sake, Alice!' she fumed. 'Leave it out, will you?'

But I wouldn't be deterred, following her down three flights of stairs and across the courtyard. She had a face like someone had died when I shoved her onto the bus and we both set off for Piccadilly to meet Handsome and ask him what the bleeding hell his game was.

'Can't you leave a girl alone to have a bit of fun with a fella? Or at least just admit you've got the hump because he asked me out to tea, not you?'

'No,' I said tetchily, crossing my arms over my chest as I took my seat next to her. 'I can't. Because it was me who he asked to dance first and I'm not going to repeat the things he was saying to me, but he weren't telling me fairy stories. He ain't someone you should be wasting your time with.'

She rolled her eyes, and we sat in silence for the rest of the journey, gazing out of the window at the rain sploshing down into the gutters.

Tea at the flaming Ritz Hotel!

I reckoned that Handsome had more front than Selfridges to ask her out to such a fancy place, right under my nose, when he'd been trying to get into my knickers all night. And now, I planned to give him a piece of my mind. At least, that's what I was telling myself but the very thought of him getting his hands on Babyface made my insides do horrible flips, like being on a fairground ride and wanting to get off.

Rows of swanky-looking cars were neatly lined up outside the grand entrance, with chauffeurs sitting there, looking bored. The snooty doorman, in a peaked cap and tailcoat with gold braids and shiny buttons, didn't look askance as we strode in, as we appeared to be just two wealthy young women about town, just popping by for a reviving cup of tea, as a break from window-shopping.

The inside of the hotel took my breath away, with its plush carpet, ornate entrance hall, gilded plasterwork, high ceilings and crystal chandeliers that sparkled. We were shown to the tearoom at the end, which had columns of marble from floor to ceiling, potted palms dotted about, a glass roof, and – no word of a lie – someone playing a grand piano. And in the middle of it all, he sat there, idly flicking through his newspaper and occasionally taking out his fob watch to check the time. His face was an absolute picture when he caught sight of both of us marching towards him.

Babyface had got herself in quite a tizz about him chatting her up at the same time as he was flirting with me. As the waiter pulled out chairs for us to sit, she threw her coat down, and glared at him. 'Well, some gentleman you've turned out to be,' she said.

He chuckled at her, and then shrugged his shoulders. 'Oh, you can't be too hard on a chap, Miss Emerald! I was surrounded by beauty, caught up in the social whirl. I must apologise if I have caused you any upset. It's wonderful to see you and Miss Diamond again. Surely, we can all be friends? Won't you both sit down?'

I was considering taking a swing at him with my handbag, to knock some sense into him, but there was something about his smile and the twinkle in his eyes which was quite charming. And as Baby sat down, sticking her nose in the air, I took the seat that was offered to me before I went all wobbly like I had in his arms on the dance floor.

'It seems your prize turn in the High Life made the headlines,' he said, brandishing the newspaper under Babyface's nose.

Her face lit up, 'You don't say!' But there was a photograph of her, posing under a headline calling her a Bright Young Thing in Fur, in the *London Evening News*. She snatched it from him and waved it under my nose, reading out loud, '*The most delightful girls in the whole of London town hit the dance floor at the High Life in Soho yesterday and the most stunning won a 25-guinea prize pot for her outfit, which included a beautiful chinchilla fur coat.*'

'I'm famous!' she gasped. I was speechless. We were already notorious as Babyface and the Bob-Haired Bandit but having her face splurged all over the newspaper wearing a stolen fur coat wasn't ever what I'd had in mind. I started to get a slightly sick feeling in the pit of my stomach and my mouth went dry.

I gave her a sharp elbow in the ribs.

'Perhaps we should be getting back. We've got our ill aunt to think about, haven't we?'

But she brushed my arm away, like I was an annoying fly, and batted her eyelashes at Handsome, who was thoroughly enjoying the attention.

'They have almost captured your beauty, Miss Emerald,' he purred. 'But in the flesh both you and Miss Diamond are so much prettier.'

'Ah, delicious,' he said, as a waitress arrived with a trolley laden with the daintiest sandwiches and tiny scones and cakes for us to choose from. 'I'm feeling rather peckish, how about you, ladies?'

I didn't have to be asked twice – I was bleeding starving, even after the fry-up. All that dancing the night before had given me quite an appetite. It wasn't often we got treated to such a delicious spread, so it would have been churlish to refuse, even if I did think Handsome was a terrible flirt with both of us. As I took a bite of the scone and glanced around at the posh folk enjoying their tea, I began to relax a little.

Babyface picked at a cucumber sandwich. She was determined to make Handsome feel bad about what he'd done. But I knew from looking at him that there was more chance of hell freezing over than him feeling a shred of remorse for leading us both up the garden path.

'I'm glad to see you both looking so radiant,' he said, as the waitress poured the tea from a huge silver teapot. I eyed the teaspoons. They were silver too. I was just working out how I might slide a few into my handbag, when I noticed that her hands were shaking, and she was turning red.

'Milk, Miss?' she queried, only just able to meet my gaze, as she sploshed some of the liquid into my bone china teacup. I was about to pick it up and take a sip, when a bevy of burly policemen came barrelling across the tearoom towards us. In the middle of them all was the shopkeeper from Bond Street, the plump one Babyface had hoisted her coat from. He didn't look jolly; in fact, he was more like a raging bull, and he was even bigger than I recalled, in a black wool overcoat, which was flapping as he stormed along, making him look like the Grim Reaper.

I leaped up to make my escape but Handsome caught me by the wrist and held onto me, for dear life. I swung at him with my other hand, balled into a fist, with the row of diamonds I was sporting as a knuckleduster. I caught him a glancing blow on the cheek, a good one too, which knocked him back and drew blood, but still he held onto me, gritting his perfect teeth. Babyface was just sitting there, horror-struck, her mouth open, but her backside still glued to her seat.

'Run!' I yelled.

She sprang to her feet, but do you know what she did then, the silly moo? She reached over and made to grab for that sodding coat, didn't she? The cozzers were on us in a split second, as ladies dropped their scones and let out cries of horror and disbelief at their afternoon tea being disrupted by such a dreadful scene. It took three policemen to hold me down and put the cuffs on, and it's fair to say my language was quite choice. But Babyface was an easier prospect, as they just lifted her clean off her feet and ignored her kicking and biting.

'These are the women, officer,' said the furrier, bristling with rage. 'And *that* is my stolen fur coat!' He picked it up and examined it.

'Yes,' he said triumphantly. 'The label is intact. It says, "Le Grand's Furriers of Bond Street!"'.

We were hauled away down the beautiful entrance hall, hollering and screaming all the way like a pair of banshees. Oh, we got a good couple of clumps round the head for our trouble, but I wasn't going to make it easy for them. And in the middle of it all, Handsome just watched and smiled, dabbing the graze on his cheek with a clean, white handkerchief. The last I saw of him, he was deep in conversation with one of the cozzers who'd arrested us, one who was wearing a smart suit rather than a blue-bottle uniform. I overheard the policeman saying, 'We rely on honest people such as yourself to tip us off about these crooks, sir. Thank you very much.' Handsome looked like butter wouldn't melt in his mouth for the way he'd grassed us up. It was sickening.

A Black Maria police wagon was waiting outside the Ritz, with a crowd gathered round it, as we were slung in the back like a couple of potato sacks. We gazed through the bars, out onto the bustling street of Piccadilly in the rain and Babyface started to sob, big fat tears rolling down her cheeks.

'You and your fucking chinchilla coat!' I spat.

CHAPTER 15

MARY

Whitechapel, February 1900

It's fair to say I'd rather have been anywhere but here, trudging through East End lanes bordered by gullies of filthy rainwater, looking for a place to stay.

My bags were weighing me down and I was weak not only from hunger but from the shock of what Ma had done, giving Jem away to the woman who hated me so much, as if he were a jewel to be bought and sold.

Up ahead, the lights were blazing in the Frying Pan pub, and an organ grinder was turning a tune on the pavement outside, with his funny little monkey tethered by a rope, skipping about in a velvet waistcoat and matching hat. Barrow boys were packing up sacks of unsold fruit and veg, and kids were running around, so many of them, with shoddy boots or none at all, hoping to swipe something for their supper. It was a game I knew well, as I'd played it in the Dials often enough as a nipper.

An old woman with a kindly face and a blanket criss-crossed over her ample bosom as a shawl called out to me from the entrance to a gloomy courtyard. 'I've a nice room for the night, love! Come on over, let's discuss a price.'

I ignored her and she yelled after me, 'Suit your bleedin' self, Miss Hoity Toity.' I wasn't born yesterday; the boarding house would be a den of thieves and I'd be stripped to my bloomers and robbed before I'd even time to show her the colour of my money. The sound of dogs barking and whining filled the cold evening air. Suddenly, the pub began to look quite inviting. I approached, stepping carefully over the cobbles, chucking the organ grinder a penny, and pushed open the doors.

Now, you couldn't say the Frying Pan was a welcoming place; in fact, I was greeted by cold stares from customers lurking in its darkest recesses, quietly sipping their pints, their faces almost obscured by pipe smoke. Others were perched at rickety tables, picking at the stodgy pastry tops of pies served in battered metal dishes. I caught a whiff of their dinners, the meaty scent mingling with tobacco. The chalkboard behind the bar said it was mutton, but it could have been anything running about those lanes on four legs from the smell of it. By now, I was so hungry that I'd eat anything, so I clasped my bags tightly under my arm and made my way to the bar to order a pie and a large brandy to wash it down with.

The barmaid was as wide as a barn door, her face flushed with two high circles of rouge as red as her low-cut calico blouse. Her hair hung in greasy ringlets, secured at the roots by filthy ribbons, and her fingers were yellowing from tobacco stains.

'You're new, ain'tcha?' she said, by way of conversation, stating the bleeding obvious with such pride, you'd think she'd discovered the secret of life itself.

I nodded politely because I didn't want to be rude. The alternative was running the gauntlet of the lowlifes from Petticoat Lane. 'I'm just passing through, looking for some friends of mine,' I began, aware that heads were swivelling in my direction to catch the gossip about what I was doing in this godforsaken place. 'Some girls from the Seven Dials headed over this way, about half a dozen of them.'

Her bottom lip set hard. 'We don't want their sort round here,' she said. 'I've heard things, bad things, about the girls from that part of town. Guttersnipes and thieves, they are. Is that where you hail from?' Calling the girls of the Seven Dials guttersnipes was a bit of a cheek, rather like the pot calling the kettle black, but I sucked it up.

'Nah,' I lied, 'I'm from Notting Hill – they've got something that belongs to me. I heard they'd hightailed it off to the East End, that's all. I'm a seamstress, I've got a trade.' A hot pie appeared through a serving hatch behind the bar, and she slammed it down in front of me.

'A likely story,' she said, fixing me with a gimlet eye.

'It's the God's honest truth,' I said. 'I did my apprenticeship sewing in the laundries up at Notting Hill, and now I take in piecework to make ends meet.' I picked up a greasy knife and fork, and began to cut into the pastry, my stomach rumbling loudly, just as a fella in the corner who was better dressed than the rest, in a smartish waistcoat and jacket, got up and sauntered towards me. He was wearing round glasses, which I'd already decided I'd knock off his face if he gave me any trouble and I needed to escape.

'I'm looking for a seamstress to help with my tailoring business,' he said, parking himself on the barstool next to me. 'The last girl I employed was a right good-for-nothing, more trouble than she was worth.'

'Bone idle!' came a voice like a foghorn, from the table where he had been sitting before.

'Yes, thank you, my sweet, I'll handle it,' he replied, waving his hand at the source of the din. 'That's my fiancée, Florrie, who helps at the front of the shop. She's a charmer with the customers, but I need someone reliable, hard-working, with nimble fingers to help me with the sewing.'

He gazed at my hands.

'You look like you fit the bill.'

'I'm a fine needlewoman, so I've been told. The laundry Missus promoted me, and I always finished my work before everyone else.' That was almost true. She would have promoted me if I'd stayed in the laundry instead of going off hoisting.

He nodded. 'Good. I can offer you board and lodging above the shop. It's just one room I have going spare, we are ever so humble in our little abode, but I'm sure it will suit your needs.' He raised his voice when he got to the bit about being humble, just to make a point to the other punters, most of whom looked like they were in need of a good bath, never mind a good tailor, in case they thought he was worth robbing, no doubt.

'I'll take the job,' I said, in between mouthfuls of meat in gravy.

This wasn't what I had in mind when I'd set off for the East End, but then nothing about my day had gone as planned, so I was just glad to have a roof over my head and somewhere to stash my belongings while I worked out my next move.

He watched me like a hawk, as I finished up every last crumb of my pie and gulped down the brandy, feeling it burning the back of my throat.

'I'm Will, by the way,' he said, offering me his hand. 'It'll be fifteen shillings a week because of the room I'm providing. Can I help with your belongings?'

He was charming enough, but I snatched them away before he could get his hands on them, just in case. 'I'll manage, thanks.' The barmaid gave him a cheery wave as we left, with his intended, Florrie, traipsing after him.

'And don't get any funny ideas,' she hissed in my earhole as we made our way across the cobbles, turning into a little lane with a row of shops, their bay windows overlooking the street. 'He's spoken for, see?' She flashed the third finger of her left hand at me, and I stifled a laugh because she had a gold band with the tiniest chip of a sapphire set into it. It was pathetic compared with my diamond sparkler, which was hidden in my carpet bag.

'You've no worries there,' I said, forcing a smile. 'I know my place. I just want some work and somewhere to stay.'

That seemed to reassure her, and she linked arms with me.

'In that case, let's hope we can be the best of friends,' she gushed. 'I didn't catch your name?'

'Millie,' I faltered, 'Millie O'Connor.' Mary Carr belonged back in the Seven Dials and the less they knew about her, the better, given today's headlines.

In the gaslight, I could just about make out a painted sign which read, 'Fine Tailoring'. His shop was one of about half a dozen tailors in the street. Will produced a key from the pocket of his waistcoat and put it in the rusty lock.

'Here's our little factory,' he joked.

The door creaked open, and I stepped inside.

I'd heard about weaver girls dying of exhaustion at their looms, and I swear if Will had been a factory gaffer, he'd have killed quite a few workers with his endless demands. I slept like a log that night, in my tiny bed, but I was woken at first light with a knock on the door, and his shouts of 'Get up!' And that was just the start of it.

The rest of the week passed in a blur of stitching and mending, which loomed over me in a giant basket on a table at the back of the shop. Florrie browbeat the customers into paying over the odds, while Will cut patterns and measured up, humming and hah-ing over seams and leg lengths. Everything was then passed to me to sew, with barely a cup of tea to keep me going. Florrie plied him with cakes, stuffing herself silly the minute the shop was empty, but she never offered me a crumb. If I left any work over for the next day, Florrie would scold me loudly and Will would stand there silently, his face contorting with annoyance, with threats to dock my pay.

Once I'd finished one lot of work, another would magically appear. That bloody basket even followed me upstairs at night, with a tap-tap on the door, just as I was about to snuff out the candle and lay my head on the pillow to get some rest. Every time I closed my eyes, all I could see was Jem smiling at me, or worse, crying for me, and I'd wake in a cold sweat, gripped by the fear of what he was going through, so in some ways, sewing until my eyes hurt or I fell asleep mid-stitch wasn't so bad.

In the few moments I had to spare each day, I'd dash out to see if I could spot any of my girls from the Forty Thieves or pick up word of their whereabouts. The smell of the East End hit you first; not just the vile stench from the rainwater stagnating in the gullies, but the tanneries, tripe shops and tallow-making, which combined to make such a stink that I had to cover my mouth to stop myself from choking.

Everyone was scraping a living from the streets, from the pasty-faced kids who picked up discarded ciggie butts, carefully removing the tobacco to be rolled and resold, to the chair-menders and basket-weavers sitting on their front steps, hard at work in all weathers. The horse dung was collected up in a bucket by a fella in an oilskin coat and taken off to the tannery to soften leather, and the rag and bone man clip-clopped his old nag through the lanes, yelling 'old iron!' at the top of his lungs in the hope of picking up a few bits of scrap metal. Fat chance of that because this lot barely had a pot to piss in.

Another time, a bloke wandered down the market shouting, 'I've got an 'orse! I've got an 'orse!' trying to sell it, only to get in a punch-up with one of the regulars from the Frying Pan pub who shouted back, 'It's only fit for the knacker's yard, mate!' Hawkers sold bits of meat they swore they'd got from the butchers at Leadenhall for a nice price, but, Lord knows, it could have been anything with a pulse.

The strangest sight was the rag fair, a maze of lanes no wider than a walking stick, where mounds of tatty old clothing and boots were heaped on tables, and sifted through and haggled over, down to the last ha'penny. But no matter how far I wandered, there was never any sign of my gang.

I'd started to feel ravenously hungry at the end of each day, and I got rather partial to those pies over at the Frying Pan pub. I thought I'd eaten too many of them or had a bit of rotten meat when I found myself chucking up in the gutter one evening outside the shop as Will peered at me in disgust through the window. But Florrie gave me a sly look, then whispered something to him, with a knowing glance. That night, there was a loud knock on my door as I was getting ready for bed and Will's face appeared.

'I'm cutting your pay to ten shillings a week, Millie,' he said, 'seeing as you're in the condition you're in, and you ain't going to get board and lodging anywhere else.'

I opened my mouth to protest. He was right, of course, although I didn't want to admit it to myself. It had been a while since I had any rags to throw on the fire.

'I knew there was something about her that wasn't quite right, from the moment I laid eyes on her!' said Florrie, looming over his shoulder and peering at me, as if I were a curiosity in the sideshows at the fun fair. 'She's gone and got herself into trouble, the saucy minx!'

I touched my belly, protectively, scared out of my wits. I thought back to the night of the Queen of Diamonds painting and the passion I'd felt in the arms of Lord Harcourt, as the horrible sick feeling swept over me again, making me retch into the jerry I kept under the bed.

I was all alone in the East End. And I was pregnant.

CHAPTER 16

MARY

Whitechapel, March 1900

It was the sight of the little ones clasping their big sisters' hands as they made their way through the lanes in their raggedy clothes that finally did for me. The way they toddled along, gazing in wonder at the sights around them, reminded me of my Jem and it was like a knife through my heart. The sound of their laughter winded me, it was so pure and full of joy. That was when I knew I was going to have to do something about it.

I'd barely had time to think about the future since the awful truth of my condition dawned on me, and Will and Florrie guessed my secret. The pair of them took delight in piling more sewing and mending into my work basket, knowing full well that I had nowhere else to go. My back ached from sitting on the hard, wooden chair for hours on end, sewing in the dim candlelight, and although the sickness had stopped, the hunger had taken over, and I never had the time or the inclination to sate it properly. When I caught sight of myself in the looking glass beside the shop counter, a haggard young woman stared back at me, her hair lank, with dark circles under her tired, blood-shot eyes. The beautiful young woman in the Queen of Diamonds painting would surely have turned her back on me in disgust at what I'd become.

I steered clear of the dairyman who came around Petticoat Lane with his churns of milk, after a few of the kids fell sick with a fever and stomach troubles. I wanted to protect the baby growing in my belly, though it was going to be born out of wedlock and would never have a chance to know its father, Lord Harcourt. The fact that he and his wife had taken my Jem, and were watching him become a young lad, only made matters worse. They'd taken the one thing in my life that mattered to me, more than wealth, more than diamonds.

Through the cold nights, as I shivered under my moth-eaten blanket in the attic above the tailor's shop, I began to plan my escape from the East End. Jem was my family and I had enough saved from my thieving to make us a fresh start, if we could get away from London to the safety of the countryside in Essex, or maybe even as far as the coast. But first I was going to have to take him back, to where he belonged, with me. In my heart of hearts, I knew there was no other future for me without him by my side.

I was ready to do the unthinkable to get my brother back.

I woke at first light, with the shouts of the knocker-up tapping on windows down the lane to get people out of bed for their shifts at the docks and the factories. I normally ignored him, waiting for Will to rattle my door and yell at me to get up and start sewing, but today I was already dressed, having slept in my clothes. I gathered my few belongings into my carpet bags and crept downstairs in my stockinged feet, before slipping on my boots. I lifted the latch, taking a final backwards glance over my shoulder, and scurried off to catch the tram up to the West End.

The first daffodils of spring were pushing through the soft earth in the neatly tended garden squares of Mayfair.

The crossing sweeper didn't recognise me with my scarf pulled up high around my collar and my bags under my arms. He had that look on his face, the one he had when he was about to chase away vagrants, but the butcher's boy came past with his pony and trap and that distracted him. The pair of them were nattering away, sharing a sly ciggie, as the door to number 7 Grosvenor Square opened, and a smart little boy in a dark navy wool overcoat, with a sailor collar shirt, shiny boots and knee breeches stepped out, holding the hand of a woman dressed head to toe in black. My heart skipped a beat. It was Jem, dressed like a little lord, making his way slowly down the steps. It had only been a matter of weeks since I last saw him, but he looked so smart, like a proper little boy. I didn't recognise the young woman, but I guessed she was a governess; there was no way Lady Harcourt was going to dirty her hands looking after him, that wasn't the way of the world with toffs. That only made me more determined to get him back. I let them get to the end of the street before gathering my bags and setting off after them, at a safe distance.

Once they reached Hyde Park, the roads were bustling with people out for a stroll, so I took my chance to get closer, catching snatches of his sing-song voice, which melted my heart. I knew it wasn't her fault, but I'd already decided that I hated the young woman who was looking after him, this governess. Her hair was pulled into a low bun and her hat was pinned at a jaunty angle. I found myself wondering if the hatpin she was using to secure it might come in handy as a weapon if I needed to snatch it. And how did she treat my little brother? Did she play games and make him laugh? Or was she cruel and strict?

They made their way down to the lake, the Serpentine, where people were already taking the rowing boats out for a turn on the water. Jem pointed, tugging at her sleeve, and started pulling her towards the water. He was a determined little fella and he'd obviously set his mind on having a go. She relented after a few minutes and they wandered towards a little hut, where a fella was taking money. Another governess was there, someone she recognised, with a baby in a pram and she peered into it as they waited in the queue, cooing over the little one, while Jem wandered off to the water's edge, to play with some ducks. I was close enough now to touch him, only a few feet away, and I started to whistle his favourite tune 'London Bridge is Falling Down'. He turned around and gazed up at me. I put my finger to my lips, to signal him to be silent, and in that moment, his eyes lit up and he ran to my side, burying his face in my skirt. There was no time to lose; I took his hand and began walking briskly towards some bushes while the governess was still distracted.

'It's hide and seek, Jem,' I whispered to him. 'We have to win, or you'll go back to that big posh house, and I won't see you no more.' He nodded, bless him, as if he understood and before long, we were crawling through the undergrowth, hunkering down, like a pair of wild animals. I hugged him tightly, scarcely able to believe that he was back in my arms.

'No matter what happens, no matter if they call for you, we can't move and we can't make a sound.' He nestled into me, hugging me, and whispered, 'Yes, Mary,' just as a shriek went up from the lake. I peeked out, catching a glimpse of the governess running like the clappers to the water, her hand clamped over her mouth. The other nanny started screaming and fellas were shouting at each other that a little boy had fallen in. Before long, two blokes were knee-deep in the lake, poking around with long poles and a policeman trotted up to see what help he could give to the governess, who had collapsed and was weeping uncontrollably. Another cozzer arrived and waded into the lake to join the search, while concerned onlookers starting shouting, 'Jeremy! Jeremy! Where are you?'

I gently put my hand over his mouth, in case he was tempted to reply, but he was such an angel he didn't make a sound. 'We're winning, Jem, you are the best at hide and seek,' I said. 'If we keep quiet, you can come away with me and we can be together forever.' He beamed at me and whispered back, 'I miss you, Mary.' I knew then I'd done the right thing, the only thing a sister could do to be with her brother, to protect him.

Oh, we were hiding for hours in those bushes. I'd packed some crusts of bread to stop him from being hungry and fidgeting. He dozed for most of the time, as I stroked his hair and it was getting dark by the time they gave up the search and the governess was led away, pale as a ghost and shaking, to convey the terrible news to her bosses, the Harcourts. When the coast was clear, I tucked him safely under my arm and we hurried through the park, crossing Carriage Drive, and stepping out to Hyde Park Corner, where rows of hansom cabbies were perched high up on the front of their cabs, their blinkered horses chomping at the bit, waiting for passengers.

The cabbie looked closely at Jem first and then addressed me, 'Where to, love?'

'Liverpool Street Station,' I said, catching my breath. It would be a long ride through the city, but it was the safest bet to get a train out of London and away to our new life together in Essex. I opened the cab door and helped Jem in, before climbing up behind him, dizzy with the thrill of our escape. The horse set off at quite a trot as I gazed out of the window at the city and the troubles we were leaving behind. With Jem safe in my arms, a wave of exhaustion and relief swept over me, and I allowed myself to be lulled by the gentle rocking of the carriage, my eyelids growing heavier.

When I opened my eyes again, at first I didn't know where I was, but as I felt the warmth of the little boy nestling in my lap, my heart skipped a beat. But for some reason, we weren't moving any more. In a split second, before I even had time to work out where we were, the door was wrenched open and I was greeted by the unmistakable and dreaded sight of a cozzer, clad in blue, reaching in to grab hold of me, shouting, 'Child snatcher!'.

They say a woman can gain the strength of ten men when she needs to, and in that moment, I lunged at him with all my might, knocking him flat on his back, biting like a wild animal. Whistles blew and shouts went up as we tussled on the ground and I was punched by what felt like an army of them, hauling me to my feet, pinning my arms behind my back. Blood was pouring from a cut on my lip, but I kicked my legs wildly, connecting with shins and groins, struggling to free myself from their grasp. The cabbie pulled Jem, howling, from the carriage, tucking him under his arm and presenting him to another policeman with pride, as if he was a haunch of venison at Christmas. 'Is this your missing boy, sir? The whole of Hyde Park was out looking for a child dressed like him this afternoon. Everyone thought he'd drowned.'

The sly sod hadn't taken me anywhere near Liverpool Street; he'd trotted around the city and taken me to Vine Street police station just off Piccadilly, to turn me over to the law. The policeman took hold of Jem, holding him under his armpits, his little legs dangling, and asked him, 'Are you Jeremy Harcourt, boy?'

He shook his head.

'Name's Jem,' he sniffed.

'He fits the description of the missing child,' said another cozzer, as I was forced to the ground and handcuffed, my face cold against the cobbles and my eyes full of tears. I heard a woman shrieking like a mad thing, squealing and wailing, 'No! Leave us be! You're wrong, he's my little brother.'

'Send an officer to Mayfair to fetch the parents, without delay,' boomed another officer.

The wailing grew louder until there was a heavy blow to the side of my head.

And then everything went black.

CHAPTER 17

ALICE

Holloway, January 1924

The prison bell clanged out at six o'clock sharp, waking me from an uneasy slumber.

The sound of cells being unlocked, and the jangling of keys reverberated along the landings, as the warders clattered up and down the spiral metal staircases that separated each floor. A few seconds later, the spy hatch in the door to my cell was pulled open, to check that I was getting out of bed. It was so cold I could see my breath in front of me, but I knew better than to lounge beneath that thin blanket one minute longer than I was supposed to because that would mean being put on report for extra work.

Besides, the mattress I was lying on was pure purgatory – hard and lumpy – and beneath that lay a plank of wood that doubled as a bed, so even at night, there was no escape from the grim clutches of the Holloway Hotel. I'd only been in the nick for a week, but it already felt like a lifetime. And as the sun rose each morning and set at the end of every day, the knot of anger inside me tightened. I stared at the drab, grey walls all around me, cursing under my breath. There was only one person to blame for this: Babyface.

Oh, she'd blubbed all the way to the police station, until I told her to pull herself together and to deny everything.

We'd found the fur coat and were just two young factory girls from the slums, dizzy with excitement about going out in the West End and it was all a huge mistake. It was a paper-thin alibi but I had to come up with something, didn't I? We'd had everything going for us, everything, with our shoplifting operation, and she'd pissed it up the wall because of her stupid desire to be the centre of attention and her weakness for that . . . I could hardly bring myself to say his name . . . that sod, Handsome.

By the time we got to Bow Street police station, we were both nursing a few cuts and bruises from our arrest at The Ritz and from the way we were yanked from that Black Maria, I knew there was worse to come. The cozzers treated us with a loathing usually reserved for murderers, never a missing a chance to get another punch or a slap in on the way to the cells. Babyface looked so shocked and broken as they split us up that I began to wonder whether she'd crack and confess to hoisting the fur and more besides. It didn't bear thinking about.

As the minutes became hours, I began to regret not getting a proper bite to eat at the hotel before we were collared, because I wasn't offered so much as a dry crust all evening. I sat through my interview with the police sergeant staring vacantly ahead as he outlined the theft charges. He pushed a confession I'd supposedly made in front of me and told me, 'Be a good girl and sign it, you might get off more lightly.' I scoffed at that, which brought another slap. It's one thing to be a thief, but it's quite another to be a bent cozzer putting words in people's mouths, ain't it? What a flaming liberty!

'You girls have made quite a name for yourselves,' he said, leaning back in his chair and stroking his moustache, eyeing me like a fox about to devour its prey. 'I suppose you're the famous Bob-Haired Bandit and that snivelling wreck down in the cells is Babyface, isn't she?'

I shrugged my shoulders, 'Haven't the foggiest idea, mate.'

He slammed his hand on the desk. 'Don't get clever with me! Your little friend didn't have much to say for herself either. You're just vermin from the slums. You've no right to be putting on airs and graces, mingling with decent folk. I've had enough of your headlines and so has the Chief Inspector. You should know your place and that is behind bars, with the rest of your kind.'

I didn't trouble myself with a reply. I could write what he understood about life for girls like me and Babyface on a postage stamp. What did he really know of the Seven Dials, the East End, the slums and sweating away doing mugs' jobs in factories or in service to the upper classes? How could he ever understand the freedom that thieving gave us? The chance for us to earn good money, and to be our own boss? Besides, I was already better acquainted with his knuckles than I wanted to be.

'Suit yourself,' he said, bristling with barely suppressed rage that I wouldn't admit anything. 'We'll see how you fare when you face justice. The judge can't wait to meet you. He's a miserable old goat and his lumbago plays up something terrible before lunch.'

Judging by the size of the crowds outside the Old Bailey the next morning, word of our arrest had got around. As we climbed down from the Black Maria, with our hands in cuffs, reporters jostled with each other to get a quote from us, shouting, 'Babyface! Bob-Haired Bandit! What've you got to say for yourselves?' and 'How was tea at The Ritz?', as flashbulbs went off.

Lady Justice, the golden statue on the top of the criminal court, loomed high above us, her gleaming sword almost piercing the sky and the scales of justice in her other hand. Just the sight of her made me tremble, because as a thief, I knew which way those scales were already tipping, and it wasn't in our favour. I kept my head low as we were bundled through a side entrance, down the flagstone steps worn smooth by generations of ne'er-do-wells before us, past the poky and damp holding cells and straight up into Number One Court, with its ornate dock, bordered by brass bars. We had a couple of cozzers at our side, in case of any funny business, but I wasn't planning any and Babyface had gone white as a sheet in any case.

I gazed up at the vaulted, barrelled ceiling and at the press and public galleries all around us, which were already filling up, the chatter echoing to make a terrible din. Lawyers swept in, black robes flapping, bundles of papers tucked under their arms, and took their seats, murmuring to each other and adjusting their grey horsehair wigs. In front of us, on a high bench, was the place where the judge would sit. There was no escaping it, we were right in the firing line. A jury filed in. They were twelve sour-faced men, who looked like they would have had us transported to Australia if that option had still been available.

'I'm scared, Alice,' whispered Babyface. 'But I swear I didn't admit a thing.'

I glared at her. I was so livid I couldn't bring myself to speak to her and she put her head in her hands and gazed at the floor in shame.

As the clock on the wall struck nine, I felt my stomach flip as the clerk strode in, yelling, 'All rise!' and a figure clad in scarlet robes swept through the doors. He winced and clutched at his back as he sat down, scowling at us, as if it was our blooming fault that he was in agony. The cozzer next to me smirked, rubbing his hands with glee at that.

In the packed public gallery, I spotted Bertha and Gert, who had come to show us their support, bless 'em. The prosecutor, a weedy bloke who barely looked old enough to shave, sprang up and began outlining the case against us to a hushed courtroom.

'May it please Your Honour, I bring here before you today two of the most cunning and persistent female thieves that London has ever seen. Together, with other persons whose identity at this point in time remains unknown, Alice Diamond and Kate Felix have acted against the interests of all purveyors of luxury goods in some of our finest stores. They are the leaders of an incorrigible gang of shoplifters who mercilessly steal furs, silks and jewels for their own gain. They have acted, therefore, against the interests of decent society.'

The jury started nodding in agreement and I noticed Bertha pulling her hat low over her eyes, just in case somebody recognised her as one of the thieves. She needn't have worried, as we were the main attraction; all eyes were on us. I gazed ahead, staring at the carved wood above the judge's leather chair, as if it was the most fascinating thing I'd ever laid eyes on, as I tried to look nonchalant.

The shopkeeper, Mr Le Grand, was next up, in the witness box, and he told a very moving story of how we'd robbed his shop, including a made-up bit about me giving him a clump around the ear as I made my getaway. There were gasps of horror at that. I turned to Babyface, to see what she made of his fib, when I noticed she was looking around the room and she'd perked up. In fact, she was smiling. It took me a few moments, because they were packed in like sardines in the public gallery, but I soon found the reason she was looking so happy. Handsome was there in the back row, smiling at her as if we were out at a dance hall and he was making eyes at her. And she was flirting with him – from the dock, for God's sake! I dug my nails into my palms to stop myself screaming and shot him the filthiest look, but he gave me a grin too, which only made me feel even more hot and bothered.

The judge adjourned for a break, heaving himself out of his chair and hobbling off, as the clerk shouted, 'The court will rise!' again. The cozzer chuckled to himself, 'That'll be his lumbago again, or perhaps his piles. I don't fancy your chances.'

When the judge returned fifteen minutes later, he sat back down, slowly and painfully, before addressing us, his reedy, thin voice barely carrying across the hushed court-room. 'And what have you to say against these charges?'

I stood up first. 'Not guilty, Your Honour. It's a case of mistaken identity. We found the coat in a cloakroom and this shopkeeper is confusing us with the real criminals. He's in shock after what happened. It ain't his fault.'

The judge flicked through some papers in front of him and then glared at me, curling his lip in disdain. 'But you already have a previous conviction for stealing, don't you, young lady?'

'That is true, Your Honour,' I replied contritely, 'but I was a foolish young girl stealing a pair of stockings back then. And I have mended my ways since.'

I could have sworn I heard him mutter, 'A likely story.'

'And you,' he said, jabbing a finger in Babyface's direction, 'what have you to say?'

Well, you could have knocked me down with a feather at that point because Babyface got up, clasping the brass rail of the dock as if she were making a star turn at one of the theatres in Drury Lane, and addressed the jury. 'I am innocent,' she gasped. 'Is it my fault that I was born poor and I couldn't resist the coat I found, quite by chance? I couldn't believe my luck! It was so lovely and warm and I did look quite nice in it, as some of you may have seen in the newspaper. But I am no thief!'

That brought guffaws of laughter from the public gallery and Handsome chuckled away to himself, his shoulders shaking, gazing at Babyface and throwing her a wink, which made her arch her back, like a cat being rubbed by its owner. I dug my nails deeper into my palms, struggling to suppress my fury. Oh, if I could have leaped over the railings and strangled him with my bare hands I would have done. And I would have enjoyed it too.

The judge banged his gavel. 'Order! I will have order in my court!'

His eyes were blazing, and an icy blast shot across the courtroom as he addressed Babyface in clipped tones. 'You look very innocent indeed, but I have no doubt that you stole this very expensive fur coat and more besides. How dare you make a mockery of this process!'

Reporters were frantically scribbling in their notebooks to get every word of his telling off. Babyface pouted like a spoilt child.

'You are a terrible, unrepentant thief. I can only assume that your co-conspirator lured you into this life of crime,' he said.

'No, Your Honour,' she replied coquettishly, batting her lashes. 'I'm as innocent as the day is long.' There were more hoots of laughter. He banged his gavel so hard that it almost knocked his glass of water flying.

'For God's sake!' I hissed at her. 'You're making this worse. Just shut up and look remorseful.'

She gazed at me, her little eyes dancing with mischief. 'We're done for, Alice, but we're famous, ain't we? So, we might as well put on a good show.'

'You're doing it all for him, ain't you?' I spat back. 'But he's the reason we're in here, you little fool! He doesn't care about you. He grassed us up to the law!'

'Well,' she said archly, 'he certainly ain't here to see *you*, is he? It was me he invited for tea at the Ritz, or have you forgotten that?' She muttered something about me being jealous of her. I would have thrown my hands up in despair at that, or given her a slap, if it hadn't been for the handcuffs.

It didn't take the jury long to decide we were both guilty as sin and the judge took great delight in handing down the sentence for grand larceny, as the clerk yelled, 'The prisoners will stand up in the dock!'

'You have terrorized this city for long enough with your wicked thefts of the most desirable items,' intoned the judge. 'There is not one shred of evidence to support your ridiculous claims to have chanced upon this most luxurious fur coat, which you stole in broad daylight from Mr Le Grand's shop, in the most appalling circumstances, including faking a pregnancy, to elicit sympathy from this very fine and caring gentleman. And so, it is with no regret whatsoever that I sentence you both to serve two years within the confines of Holloway Prison.'

There were gasps at that. That was the kind of sentence you might get for robbing a bank, not nicking a fur coat! Babyface turned to the public gallery and shouted, 'It won't cure me! It'll only make me a worse villain!', lapping up the cries of disbelief at her outburst, as if she were receiving applause from the audience.

The clerk called for order. The judge, very slowly, deliberately, stopped and took a sip of water, savouring it, before adding, 'With hard labour and no remission.'

I sank back onto the wooden bench in the dock, closing my eyes, dizzy with shock.

I willed the floor to open up and swallow me whole, because going straight to Hell would have been preferable. The rest of it was a blur: being led down the steps, bundled back into the police wagon and carted off to prison with all the other poor cows – drunks, prostitutes, debtors.

We were unloaded inside the walls of Holloway Prison. It looked like a castle, with buttresses and battlements, but this was no fairy tale. The windows were barred and the warders' faces were set as hard as the grey stone of the prison. They hurried us, still in handcuffs, down into the cavernous entrance hall, where a meagre fire was burning in the grate and wooden stalls were lined up along one wall, like horse boxes. Our cuffs were removed, with a warning that any failure to behave would have severe consequences for our time in jail.

The chief warder, a brute of a woman, slapped an ebony truncheon in her palm, as she boomed, 'Do as you're told and you'll be treated fairly. Cross me, or any one of my staff, and you'll regret it.'

We were told to strip off in the horse boxes, removing not only our clothes but what was left of our dignity. After the doctor had a good look at me, checking every orifice and ensuring I wasn't infested with lice, I was handed a bundle of clothes. I pulled on the undershirt cut from the scratchiest flannel cloth and slipped the shapeless blue dress of the hard labour division over my head, topping it off with the hated prison cap. A screw came in and gave me a badge with a number on it, to be worn at all times, and I stepped out to face Babyface, drowning in her outfit, with boots that looked so big, she could have had a pair of oars in each and rowed up and down the River Thames in them.

Her eyes filled with tears. 'I'm so sorry, Alice, please, please forgive me.' She was shaking like a leaf, looking more like a lost child than the brazen bandit who had cheeked the judge in the Old Bailey and reduced the press to hoots of laughter with her antics.

But despite her despair, I just couldn't bring myself to speak to her.

And when I finally did, as we were marched up to the landings to our cells, it was only to whisper, 'You're on your own now, you silly bitch.'

CHAPTER 18

ALICE
Holloway, April 1924

A pile of old rope lay at my feet. I clasped it, pulling a length into my lap as I started to unpick it, wincing as the cuts and grazes on my fingers began to bleed again.

Oakum-picking – unravelling filthy, oily ropes to make mats or stuff prison mattresses – was a punishment from the days of Queen Victoria herself but we were still at it, day after day, because it was so effective. It was the mainstay of our hard labour for those first few months. It made you go out of your mind with boredom, and it had the added bonus for the powers that be, of making you really suffer at the same time. Two for the price of one, so to speak. We sat for six hours at a time, in rows on rickety wooden chairs that made you feel every bone in your backside, picking away, knowing that tomorrow would bring more of the same.

Hard labour was a cruel sentence, meted out by courts when they wanted to make an example of someone for their crime, to really make them suffer with harsher conditions: smaller cells, fewer privileges, and tough prison jobs designed to break the spirit. As the screws wandered up and down, ensuring there was no talking and everyone was doing their fair share, I dwelled, as I always did, on the stupidity of Babyface. Weeks had passed and still the anger boiled away inside me, growing like a cancer. If she hadn't made such a show of herself in the Old Bailey, if she'd just kept quiet or looked a bit meek, we would still have got a long stretch but at least it would have been without this torture.

We'd had it all; we'd had the West End in the palm of our hands, living like royalty, robbing the shops with plenty of money to spare and now we'd lost it. But when I really thought about it, what hurt the most was that we hadn't been caught red-handed, scarpering down the stairs with a fur coat in our knickers or hightailing it out of a jeweller's shop with a trayful of sparklers. At least there was some honour in that. Instead, we were hooked on a line like a couple of stupid fish.

We'd been nicked because she was flaunting that chinchilla coat in the newspaper, drawing attention to it, because she'd been dazzled by that bloke Handsome and I'd been powerless to stop it. He'd been suspicious of us from the start, I could see that now, recalling the way he smirked at us, knowing we didn't quite fit in with the debutantes and the aristocrats in the High Life, when he offered us a smoke. And there was no doubt he'd shopped us to the cozzers and set us up at The Ritz and I hadn't seen that coming either.

Oh God, he haunted my dreams, with his twinkling eyes. But the rage I felt, as I picked away at that pile of old rope, was really reserved for Babyface. The way she'd wanted to impress him so badly that she put herself in that bloody fashion show in her sodding fur coat and got her photo in the paper. Not to mention playing to the gallery in the Old Bailey as if it was a night at the varieties. She'd dragged us both into it. She'd dragged me into this flaming prison, despite all my carefully laid plans to build a nice little earner and I hated her for it.

And, as it turned out from the moment when we set foot in Holloway, so did the rest of the prison.

It's amazing how word of your criminal exploits gets around the nick without you having to brag about it. The warders had read all about Babyface and the Bob-Haired Bandit in the pages of the *London Evening News* and were fully up-to-date with the court case, that much was clear from the moment we arrived.

'Don't think you'll find any fancy fur coats in here, ladies,' they chuckled, brandishing the newspaper under our noses.

'And any stupid showing off in here is likely to put you in solitary, my girl!'

The headlines were worse than I'd imagined. I caught a glimpse, my heart sinking down to my ridiculous prison boots, as I read '**BOB-HAIRED BANDIT AND BABYFACE JAILED AFTER FURS THEFT AND COURT OUTRAGE!** *Judge hands down stiff sentence after pair of shameless thieves who terrorized London show contempt in court.*'

The screws had their favourite prisoners, their narks, their informers, who kept them in the loop on who was breaking the rules, planning an escape or brewing hooch in their cells. And in return, they brought them newspapers, or told them all the gossip from the world outside these walls. It was gratefully received by old lags and fresh faces alike, because prison is all about the pecking order. There are certain things you only know once you have been through it. Criminals in the nick have to decide who to tread carefully around and who needs to be taken down a peg or two and what they can glean about your criminal activities plays a part in that. There are leaders and there are followers. Anyone who thinks they are better than the rest, or who draws attention to themselves, is fair game.

And, as Babyface found out, there are victims.

The other prisoners wasted no time in letting her know how unwelcome she was. Maybe because I was taller, stronger and I'd been in here before, I was spared the worst of it. And the fact that I clearly wasn't talking to her was taken as a sign that I wouldn't get involved if she got singled out for special treatment, the kind of treatment that women in Holloway just love to dish out to do something with all their pent-up anger about being behind bars, angry with something and everything.

Now, the food at Holloway was bleeding terrible at the best of times but as any idiot will tell you, no matter how disgusting it is, you have to eat to keep your strength up. Breakfast, if you could call it that, was a lump of dark brown, stale bread so hard that you'd break your teeth on it and a smear of rancid butter. Somehow there was never much of that left for Babyface. We washed it down with a mug of watery, cold tea before setting off to pick oakhum. Lunch was a travesty called pea broth. I watched one of the women who was doling it out spit into Babyface's bowl before slopping a meagre portion in there. Mid-week, we were treated or punished, depending on your viewpoint, by a lumpy suet pudding to accompany whatever scraggy meat had been chucked in a pot with a carrot and a bit of potato to create a stew. Babyface was not only given the smallest portions, she was shunned by everyone except the women who were in for child-killing or murdering their other halves. Those poor cows had no hope of ever getting out and it was seen as bad luck to talk to them because they were going to hang, so they'd take what comfort they could in conversations with those who'd been given the cold shoulder.

With every passing day, deprived of friendship and a sense of belonging as well as nourishment, Babyface seemed smaller, quieter, more insignificant, swimming around in her too-big prison uniform and clumpy boots. She shuffled listlessly along the corridors after work, to sit on her own in her cell. She ate staring at whatever she'd been dished up, her eyes brimming with tears. With every insult she was subjected to – and there were many – she became thinner and thinner, her complexion as grey as the prison walls. Still I refused to talk to her, the gulf between us widening daily, as I was welcomed into secret gangs sharing gossip and laughter, which were like the sun coming out when we walked endlessly in circles around the yard for daily exercise. Babyface was the weed we trampled, the stone we kicked out of the way.

I couldn't reach out to her now because it would harm my position in the prison hierarchy and, anyway, she'd brought it on herself, hadn't she, with her hoity-toity ways, big mouth and her lust for fame?

There were a couple of moments when we were so close that I could reach out and touch her and she turned to me, gazing imploringly with eyes that were sunken in her bony little face. I set my mouth in a hard line and glared back at her, until she turned away.

Sometimes, when I lay in my cell after lights out, I could hear her crying softly in the cell next door and I put my pillow over my head to muffle the sound. When uneasy sleep finally came, I saw her twirling on the dance floor, dressed in a silk beaded gown, her face glowing with excitement, as Handsome held her in his arms as if she were the most precious jewel. When they kissed, as they always did in my dream, I felt a stab of jealousy and anger.

How dare she choose him over me? I was the one who had picked her up from the gutter and extended the hand of friendship. She was the only thing, the only person I'd ever really cared for, and we were meant to be a team. But at the first sight of a good-looking bloke, she'd turned her back on me, on our gang, on everything I'd worked so hard to create with her.

And how dare he move me around that bloody dance floor like a painted puppet when all the while he was plotting our downfall?

How dare they want each other, yearn for each other, and exclude me? What gave them the right to do that? I whispered it in the pitch black of those Holloway nights, as the moonlight glinted on the high, barred window of my cell, and nobody was listening.

'Why did you do that, Babyface, when I wanted you so badly?'

The criminals weren't the only ones in Holloway who had a pecking order. I worked out pretty quickly that the screws also had a hierarchy. It wasn't just to do with age and experience; it was about personal likes and dislikes. I kept my eyes peeled, like a foot soldier looking for gaps in a knight's armour, and before long, I'd picked the runt of the litter, a bit of a loner, called Fanshawe.

Now, Fanshawe had a youthful look about her – a bit too innocent if you ask me – and an unremarkable face, almost featureless, with small, round eyes and thin lips, as if she didn't want to stand out or make a fuss about existing. Hazarding a guess, I'd say she was in her mid-twenties, which in marriage terms meant she was practically an old maid, left on the shelf. As I went around the prison, I noticed that none of the other screws talked to her, they didn't spend time trading gossip in their breaks or include her in their spiteful schemes to torment prisoners who'd crossed the line and misbehaved. She was excluded from all the usual fun of the prison that the rest of them got off on.

It was Fanshawe who was given the graveyard shifts, the bleary-eyed early morning starts, the Bank Holidays and weekends to work on our wing. Her shoulders slumped when the other screws turned their backs and offered each other a nice cup of tea and she was excluded from the invite, day after day. So, she was the one I made the focus of my brightest smile each morning. I held the door open for her and volunteered for extra cleaning duties just to get on her good side, even when my back ached from unravelling those ropes. Before long, she was acknowledging me in the mornings and although she never cracked a smile, there was an unmistakable twinkle in her eye when our paths crossed.

I've never been a grass, but I tipped her the wink about a few bits of gossip I'd overheard – who had the most ciggies stashed under her mattress, that sort of thing – just so she could show her chief that she was reliable and that she had control of her prisoners. The cell raid she organised was very successful, netting more than I'd imagined, because some of the girls had even got hold of hatpins and gawd only knows what damage they could have done with those. And before long, thanks to me, she wasn't getting left out of the tea breaks, although she always tended to hang around the edge of the crowd and listened to the chatter of the other screws. They tolerated her presence because the chief had more time for her now.

Fanshawe was the one I mentioned when I wrote to Gert and Bertha, asking them to visit me and telling them I was missing my Aunt Emily. I didn't have an aunt called Emily, of course. As everyone round our way in South London knew, it was just prison slang, a way of asking for snuff so that I could trade and start making my life a bit easier. I'd had enough of hard labour and being a nobody in Holloway and with Fanshawe on my side, now was the time for things to change.

It was one of those rainy Aprils, when it came down in stair rods, and Bertha and Gert turned up at visiting time looking like a pair of drowned rats. They'd brought me a pot plant, which was very kind, and quite creative, as I'd guessed they'd buried a packet of snuff in the soil. Cakes were a no go because the screws would smash them to bits looking for weapons, and neither of the girls could cook in any case.

Bertha plonked it down on the table between us, as the visiting room filled up with relatives. Occasionally, a child would reach out to be hugged by her mother, who was like a stranger in a prison dress, and the warders would shriek, 'No touching!' and slam down their truncheons on the table to make their point. Sobs were stifled, expressions of love were whispered and news from the outside was devoured hungrily.

Fanshawe smirked when she saw the plant. 'An aspidistra, Alice, how thoughtful your friends are.' And she let them hand it over to me by way of thanks because I was her little nark, or so she thought.

'You ain't looking too bad, Alice,' said Gert. 'But I can't say the dress suits you.'

I was in no mood for joking.

'How's business?' I said curtly. 'Have you been shopping lately?'

They looked at the floor, shamefacedly.

'That's the thing,' Bertha began, 'the Partridges have gone back to the factory because their mum don't want them in the nick, she says it'll kill her.'

'But you've been busy, ain't you?' I said. 'Gamages and Selfridges will have some lovely things in for the warmer weather.' I'd been imagining shops filled with rails of silk dresses and beautifully cut cotton blouses. The desire to hoist was still an itch I had to scratch.

Gert lowered her voice. 'We ain't been hoisting since you got caught. We just ain't got the bottle for it without you.'

I rolled my eyes. 'So what've you been doing to earn your keep? I don't want to lose that flat in Queen's Buildings! God knows, we worked hard enough to get it. You'll have to pay the rent somehow.'

'It's fine,' Bertha soothed. 'Gert's working as a barmaid and I've been doing some shifts down at the wastepaper factory. We've still got a bit of money put by and we ain't exactly painting the town red without you.'

'How's Babyface?' said Gert, changing the subject before I could give them an earbashing for not having the nerve to pinch so much as a few pairs of stockings.

A lump formed in my throat. I cleared it.

'She's fine,' I lied. 'Prison diet don't exactly agree with her, and the work's a bitch but she's surviving.'

Bertha glanced around. 'I thought she might have come along to see us, that's all.' She pulled a bar of chocolate from her coat pocket. 'It's just, I bought this for her 'cos I know she likes Cadbury's.'

I took it from her before anyone spotted, avoiding her gaze as I replied, 'The screws had her doing some job or other, but I'll see she gets it.' My hands were shaking as I tucked the treat inside my pocket. How could I begin to explain it all to them – the hurt, the anger, shunning Babyface and what I was doing to survive? The truth was, I couldn't. Visiting time came and went, and I didn't even try.

That's the thing about prison. It changes you.

I went in a thief, and it made me a liar.

CHAPTER 19

ALICE
Holloway, April 1924

I sat in my cell that evening with Bertha's chocolate bar burning a hole in the pocket of my dress.

After lights-out, I quietly unwrapped it, and broke a piece off, tasting the sweetness, rolling it around my tongue, thinking of Babyface, hungry and lonely in the cell next door. Then, I took another piece and another, cramming them quickly into my mouth until I was almost drooling. I forced myself to swallow the sticky, gooey lumps, as the happy times we'd spent hoisting up in Gamages flashed before me. Before I knew what was happening, tears were rolling down my cheeks and the knot of anger in my stomach tightened, growing so big, I felt like I was choking.

There was only one thing for it. I grabbed the jerry from under the bed and stuck my fingers down my throat, retching hard, as bitter, brown liquid splurted out into the pot in front of me and the feeling of rage began to subside. I lay back on the mattress, exhausted, my shoulders shaking as shame crept over me like a thin blanket, offering no comfort.

My head was pounding the next morning and my mouth was as dry as the desert as we slopped out our cells, folded away the mattresses and filed down to breakfast. I had my little packet of snuff tucked safely inside my pocket. I couldn't leave it in the cell in case it was searched, but with Fanshawe on my side, I reckoned it was the best bet to keep it with me. The prison governor was there, beaming at us like a kindly headmistress, and she waited until we were all seated before clearing her throat. Nobody dared take so much as a sip of water or a bite of their stale bread before she'd had her say, because this was no ordinary occurrence. The governor was a bit like Jesus. You believed he existed, but you never saw him and when you did, it usually meant you had to pray quite hard for forgiveness.

'Girls,' she began, which was a ridiculous thing to say. Some of the prisoners were old enough to be her grandmother. 'Today is a very important day as the Prison Inspection Committee will be doing the rounds and so I want to show them the very best that Holloway has to offer for its inmates. We will be going to the craft and education classes for the second-division prisoners, but also touring the prison more generally, to see you all hard at work, to show that you are reforming and spending your time in here most usefully.'

The notion that picking away at old rope was useful was just a flaming lie, but I couldn't say anything because I didn't want to get my teeth knocked out by a warder's truncheon for insubordination.

'To that end, I need a number of volunteers for extra cleaning duties,' she added primly.

My hand shot up, like a firework zooming skywards on Bonfire Night, because frankly I'd shovel shit if it meant getting away from oakhum-picking. Fanshawe selected me and about half a dozen of the hard labour lot, including Babyface, who looked more relieved than any of us to be getting away from the piles of old rope.

'Very good,' said the governor, clapping her hands together. 'Please get on with your breakfasts and do your very best today. I am relying on you to show the Holloway spirit!' She bounded off, back to her office, to prepare for her important visitors. I'd never seen an inspection committee before, but I'd heard that a bunch of do-gooders and bleeding heart liberals took it upon themselves to come around, poking their noses in where they weren't wanted, every few months. The governor had to let them in, but she was very careful about what they saw. It was a change from the usual routine for us all, which was a bonus as far as I was concerned.

Fanshawe marched us down to the laundry block to collect cleaning supplies – mops, buckets, bleach, polish and scrubbing brushes – and we trooped back to the circular centre of the prison, with its arched iron roof, which was the governor's pride and joy. All the wings radiated out from this central point, like the rays of the sun, and the floor was always waxed and gleaming. The whole prison could be seen from this area, connected by metal catwalks and spiral staircases and it gave visitors a sense of the order of the place. Any prisoner who crossed that centre without the permission of a prison officer would find themselves losing privileges and in solitary for a day or two. Before long, we were down on our knees, scrubbing and polishing.

'I want to see your faces in it by the time you are done,' said Fanshawe tartly, the soles of her shoes squeaking as she walked in front of us, observing us closely. We worked slowly, diligently, in a long line, inch by inch. But we were only just finishing when the visiting party appeared, which made Fanshawe a bit flustered.

'Get up, you lazy lot!' she hissed. 'Stand up straight and look smart!'

We leapt to our feet, and one of the others accidentally elbowed me as she was hauling herself up, and I fell forward. There was no malice in it. But the packet of snuff, tightly wrapped in brown paper, flew out of my pocket and skittered across the polished floor, landing at the governor's feet. There was a sharp intake of breath among the Prison Inspection Committee, with much twitching of moustaches and clasping of handbags.

'What's this?' boomed the governor, bending down to pick it up.

She held it up and glared at us.

'Whose is this packet?'

The question hung in the air for a moment.

Before anyone knew what was happening, Babyface had piped up, 'It's mine, Miss.' There was only one other prisoner separating us, and she must have known that package came from my pocket.

The governor stiffened. She began to unwrap it, peering at it closely. 'This is snuff tobacco, isn't it?'

Babyface shuffled her feet and stared at the gleaming floor.

'The prisoner will answer!' barked Fanshawe, going quite red, her hand on her truncheon. The governor turned to the committee members who were murmuring amongst themselves. 'I can assure you, finding contraband of this nature in Holloway is a very, very rare occurrence. The miscreant will face severe sanctions.'

'Yes, Miss,' whispered Babyface, quaking in her boots. 'I'm very sorry, Miss.'

The governor marched over to her. She was a tall woman, and she loomed over Babyface. 'Where did you get this?'

Babyface shook her head. I made to step forward, to confess it was mine, but Fanshawe looked at me with such a pained expression that I thought better of it.

'Can't say, Miss,' said Babyface.

'Can't say or won't say?' said the governor brusquely. She turned to Fanshawe. 'Solitary confinement, two weeks, and bread and water. Let me know when she is ready to talk.' Other screws appeared and they fell on Babyface like a pack of hungry wolves, grabbing hold of her arms, so that she was practically lifted off her feet as they took her away to the punishment block.

And with that, the governor and the Prison Inspection Committee marched across our floor, on their way to do more good.

What happened with Babyface was the talk of the entire prison, but if any of the others in our cleaning team had spotted who had really dropped the package, they weren't saying. Fanshawe knew right enough, and she made a point of lingering by my cell door at lights out.

Even my cocoa, which was one of the best things about Holloway, because even on hard labour you still got a lovely warm cupful to drink every evening, tasted rancid now because I was so worried about Babyface. I heard some footsteps as I warmed my hands with the tin cup and suddenly, the hatch on my cell door was pulled back.

'Alice,' she hissed, 'you'd better not breathe a word of who that snuff really belonged to or how it got into this jail. Do you understand?'

'It ain't right,' I hissed back. 'It was my fault, not her's. I should be in the punishment block. I swear I won't drop you in it, but I need the governor to know the truth. I'm guilty.'

'I can't do that,' she murmured. 'It could lead back to me and then I'd be for it. Sorry, Alice, you know the rules.'

'Please!' I begged. 'I'll be your nark, I will do anything you say if you just give me the chance to take Babyface's place down there.'

'Your little pal is very loyal, she won't tell the guards a thing, so I've heard, but let's just hope she keeps her trap shut. For your sake as well as mine.'

I bristled at that.

'You can rely on her to keep quiet,' I said. I was only beginning to realise it, but Babyface was loyal to a fault. 'Just tell the governor that someone told you that the package of snuff fell from my pocket. You can do that, can't you?'

'I'll think about it,' said Fanshawe, pulling the metal hatch shut.

I saw Babyface in the days that followed, shuffling around the exercise yard on her own, as we were coming back in from our turn out there. It sounds medieval, but bread and water really did mean just that, and I could tell she was weak from hunger, every little step she took taking so much of her energy. The punishment block guards were the worst in the whole nick because they really enjoyed making prisoners suffer. A woman could go mad in solitary and sometimes they did. One tried to bash her own brains out on the cell floor and had to be carted off to the asylum. But not Babyface, she took it all, remaining tight-lipped in the face of their bullying attempts to get her to own up. When it rained, we were hurried around the exercise yard, but those bitches made her stand outside for hours, getting soaked through, so Fanshawe told me.

'She's like the little tin soldier standing out there,' she said, with a note of admiration in her voice, as I came back from supper one day. 'I don't know where she gets the strength because there is barely a picking on her.'

'She's had a tough life and she's very brave,' I replied, feeling tears prick my eyes. 'But surely even you can see she's getting weaker? It ain't too late to let me take her place. The governor might reward you for finding the real culprit.'

She put her finger to her lips as some other warders walked past and then murmured, 'Just keep quiet, Alice – you know it's too risky to speak up now.'

What the hell had I done? I'd been so consumed by rage at getting caught and so jealous of Babyface's affection for Handsome, that I'd cut myself off from her. But she was my one true friend, the one person in this life who trusted me and who believed in me. I'd promised to always look after her.

I'd let her down and now she was standing out there in the pissing rain for me, to protect me, the one person who had been so bloody mean to her all these weeks. I decided there and then, I would make it right, I'd make it up to her, take her back under my wing, protect her. I'd fight to get her whatever she needed in this hellhole to make her life bearable, even if it meant I got into trouble for it. The moment I said that to myself, the knot of anger inside me started to unravel. It was a relief, not hating her anymore, because I knew then that I loved her, more than anyone or anything in this world.

My heart skipped a beat on the final day of her solitary confinement because I knew Babyface would be returning to the wing, and everyone was planning to make a bit of a fuss of her. The fact that she'd been down the punishment block was something of a badge of honour, even for the most hard-hearted of the prisoners who'd delighted in taunting her. A few of them had even been saving some bread and bits of cheese to give her, to help build her back up again, because the word on the wing was that she was like a walking skeleton.

Supper came and went but still there was no sign of her.

Just before lights-out, the hatch on my cell door was pulled back and Fanshawe's face appeared. Even through that small gap, I could see she was white with shock. 'It's your friend,' she began. 'She's very sick. The governor's been informed, and they've called a doctor. She's in the hospital wing. It's serious, Alice, they think it's pneumonia.'

'Please,' I whispered. 'You've got to let me see her.'

She'd already closed the hatch. I ran to the door, hammering. 'Please, you have to let me see Babyface! Take me to her! Please!'

But her footsteps echoed down the metal walkway, leaving me alone with my guilt.

The prison chaplain ran towards the hospital wing early the next morning as we set off for work. I pleaded again with Fanshawe to let me see Babyface and by lunchtime, she'd put a request in with the governor, who consented. Everyone in the dining hall exchanged glances as Fanshawe led me away because hospital wing visits were about as rare as hell freezing over.

'You'd better not forget I did this for you,' Fanshawe muttered under her breath as she marched me along. 'And you'd better keep your trap shut about how that snuff got inside these four walls.'

She produced a key from a bunch on the belt at her waist and unlocked the door to the hospital. It was so quiet inside, you could have heard a pin drop and the whole place reeked of disinfectant, with rows of beds lined up, sending me back to the times I'd been to see poor Lily after her accident at the jam factory. But now, the reason my friend was sick was all down to me and that weighed heavily. One bed had the curtains drawn tightly around it and I knew Babyface was in there because the chaplain came out, clutching his Bible.

'Keep it brief,' he said to me. 'She is very ill indeed.'

Nothing prepared me for what I saw. Her cheekbones were so sunken that her skin looked like yellowing parchment and her lips were cracked and dry. Her breathing came in sickening rasps, which made her tiny frame shake beneath the sheet covering her. I took a cloth from the side, dipped it in a jug of water, and pressed it to her lips to try to give her a drop of moisture.

Her eyelids fluttered open.

'Baby, it's me, Alice,' I said, kneeling beside her, holding onto her hand, which was icy cold. The tips of her fingers were turning blue. 'It's all my fault, please forgive me.'

She looked right at me, with a light in her eyes, the same light she always used to have. It was like a little match burning in the dark. 'I'm sorry, Alice,' she croaked, 'for all of it. I'm not strong enough.'

'No,' I said. 'You are, you can make it. We're going to get you well again, that's what the matron said.' But we both knew I was lying. She took another painful breath. 'All I ever wanted was to impress you,' she rasped. 'Not him.'

Then she gasped once more, closed her eyes and left me.

They buried her before dawn in a corner of the prison garden, wrapped in the sheet she'd died in, beside those murderers she'd been forced to talk to because I'd shunned her. I hated that. It wasn't right for her to be beside a bunch of killers.

I was sickened by everything I'd done, so sickened I couldn't bring myself to eat and when I did, I'd put my fingers down my throat and bring it all back up again. It wasn't long before Fanshawe noticed my rancid breath and my gaunt looks. She got me transferred to the laundry, where I spent my days heaving wet sheets through the mangle.

'The change will do you good, the governor says,' she told me. 'And if you don't start eating properly, Alice, I'll have to tell the doctor and he'll come and stick a tube down your gullet like they did with the suffragettes, to force some nourishment into you.'

I knew she wasn't making idle threats because the death of two healthy prisoners would mean difficult questions from the Prison Inspection Committee, and the governor wasn't going to allow that to happen.

'Kate,' I whispered her name, half expecting her to answer, but all I heard was the tolling of the prison bell. I ached for her; her laughter, her smile, and her stupid way of breaking all the rules and sticking two fingers up to everything and getting away with it. Babyface could cheat everything but death.

I hated myself so much, I wanted to join her in that hole in the ground. Whenever we were on exercise, I'd linger by the mound of earth which marked her resting place, whispering my apologies, hoping that somehow, she'd know how sorry I was.

That I'd never forget her.

And I'd never forgive him.

But above all, I'd never forgive myself.

CHAPTER 20

MARY

Vine Street, March 1900

I woke up on the floor of a tiny cell, as daylight streamed through the bars on a grimy window high above me. I hauled myself up, my head throbbing, touching a lump the size of an egg on the side of my face where I'd been whacked by the cozzer. There was a bucket on the floor, for prisoners to use as a jerry. I picked it up and started bashing it against the iron door, making a fearful racket, shouting, 'Give me back my brother!'

A voice boomed down the corridor, 'Hold your tongue, you vixen!'

'He's my brother, you've no right to take him from me!' I shouted back.

My arms were covered in bruises and every bone in my body ached from the way I'd fought to keep Jem, but still I found the energy to cry out for him. The door swung open, and I came face-to-face with half a dozen policemen, every one of them looking for a fight. I took a few paces back into the cell.

'Not so loud, now, are you?' said the first. I recognised him as the one who'd yanked me from the carriage last night. He pulled out his truncheon and held it to my throat, blocking my airway, making me gasp for breath.

'This is how we treat child-stealers,' he smirked, pushing

me up against the cold bricks. I was powerless to resist, weak from exhaustion and hunger.

'Steady on,' said the cozzer behind him, 'she's up in front of the judge in an hour. We don't want her looking too bashed up or he'll send her off to hospital.'

That made him think twice. He tucked the truncheon back into his thick, leather belt.

'Jeremy Harcourt was legally adopted by Lord and Lady Harcourt, as you well know,' he said icily. 'They have the proof and we have seen it. The boy's too young to understand what's going on but he knew his governess well enough. He's safely back in Mayfair, where he belongs.'

I sank to my knees in despair. 'No! It ain't right.'

The second policeman stood over me. 'You're not of the class to be able to say what is or isn't right, girl! Your mother made a deal for the good of her child, who she couldn't care for, and Lord and Lady Harcourt rescued him from a life in the Seven Dials. He's better off without her – or you, for that matter.'

The first added, 'We know who you are, Mary Carr, and you can't just go stealing a boy because he takes your fancy! He's not one of the furs you like to pinch from Selfridges! Now stop yelling and making a fuss, and be a good girl, and I'll think about bringing you a nice cup of tea and a piece of bread. How about that?'

He brushed some hair away from my face, making me wince, as he touched the bruises.

'I like a girl with a bit of spirit in her, but you, my dear, are like a wild horse that needs breaking in,' he chuckled. Then he whispered, 'And if I wasn't in such a hurry to get you up before the beak, I might even oblige.'

I glared at him but said nothing because I wasn't sure I could take another beating.

I sat with my head in my hands, defeated, as the pair of them left and the cell door clanged shut.

Nothing had prepared me for the crowds. They were lined up outside the prison screaming abuse when I was led out to the Black Maria in handcuffs, with a policeman at either side of me. They jostled and jeered, baying at me, because word had gone around that I'd stolen a child. My community lived in fear of the kind of people who did that; the ones who spirited them away, to be abused by posh folk in their sordid games in their country mansions, or even abroad. I wasn't like that. He was my brother and I'd only wanted to make a fresh start in Essex, for pity's sake.

'You evil cow, Mary Carr!' screeched a girl I recognised from the laundry, spitting at me. 'I hope you rot in jail!' A few of them waved newspapers at me: '**BOY STOLEN FROM PARK BY THIEF QUEEN**'. There was no point trying to give them my side of the story, that I was the one who'd been robbed by that evil witch in Mayfair. I'd already decided to save that for the judge, in the hope that he'd be merciful.

It was more of the same when I arrived at Bow Street magistrates and I was bundled from the van under a torrent of shouts about what the good folk of Soho would do to me if only they were given half a chance. The dark, narrow corridor beneath the courthouse was horribly familiar to me, as I was bustled along it, and up the staircase into the dock. It was where poor old Polly had been convicted of larceny and I'd escaped jail by the skin of my teeth only a few months before.

The courtroom was full to bursting when I was led up the stairs from the cells into the wooden dock. But this time, it wasn't just the usual lowlifes from the Seven Dials on the benches. There were gentlemen in there, their hair neatly slicked back, wearing suits cut from fine cloth, with starched white collars and cuffs. They viewed me with curiosity, as if I was an animal in the zoo. Murmurs rippled through the public gallery. 'That's her!' and 'She's the one in his painting.' A few of them twizzled the ends of their moustaches, smirking in my direction.

I stared defiantly ahead. What did they know of my situation? Was it a crime to want to be with my brother? Surely it was my mother who was the criminal, having wasted her life on drink and then sold him as if he were wares at the market, when he was my flesh and blood. I'd bathed him, dressed him, fed him and cared for him for as long as I could remember. If I had a crust of bread, I'd give it to him and go hungry. What did they know of misery and hunger? Of rubbing his little hands to get warmth back into them and giving up my blanket at night to keep him cosy, when the cold was biting worse than the bed bugs?

The judge swept in wearing his scarlet robes and long horsehair wig, with a horribly familiar look. He was the same beak as last time, the one who'd jailed Polly. My heart sank. The prosecution tucked his thumbs into his waistcoat as he eyed me, licking his lips like a tiger about to devour its prey. He was clearly relishing the prospect of playing to a full house because child-stealing was better than his usual fare of punch-ups and petty thieving. Besides, the audience were a finer class of people too; the quality one might even say.

I gripped the edge of the dock as I stood there, preparing myself for his clever words that would paint me as a villain. And then they walked in at the last minute, arm in arm, and I felt my knees buckle.

'Stand up straight, girl!' hissed the cozzer, 'or you'll be facing a longer prison sentence! The judge will not tolerate disrespect.'

I mumbled something about feeling dizzy.

Lord Harcourt's hair was still a riot of curls, his face still so handsome, but he had a haunted look as he guided his wife to her seat near the front of the court. He avoided my gaze entirely, but she gave me a hard stare, and – there was no mistaking it – a triumphant smile, which made her thin lips curl at the corners. She sat with her head held high, elegant, wealthy, untouchable; the woman who had taken the one thing in this life who meant more to me than diamonds, my brother Jem.

'The accused will stand up straight while the charges against her are outlined,' said the judge coldly. The cozzer shot me a look that said, 'I told you so.'

The prosecution took this as his cue to give the performance of a lifetime. 'I bring before you today the most wicked, cunning and evil girl, Mary Carr, lately of the Seven Dials, who has conspired to steal a child from his benefactors, Lord and Lady Harcourt, of Grosvenor Square, Mayfair.'

'And what,' said the judge, his eyes boring into me, 'is the relationship of this kidnapped boy to this young woman before my court?'

'Mary Carr was raised with the child, a boy called Jeremy, in the slums of the Seven Dials. Their mother was a drunk, and therefore unable to care for him. But he was adopted recently by Lord and Lady Harcourt, who were able to see good in the innocent child, and pledged to raise him as their own.

'This angered Mary Carr, who is known to many in her community as an inveterate thief and persistent shoplifter, the Queen of Thieves, and she determined to prevent her brother from enjoying his new, more privileged life, and to steal him away from his new home.'

There were gasps of horror from the public benches.

'No!' I shouted. 'That's a pack of lies! It was never like that!'

The judge banged his gavel. 'I will have silence in court!'

He went on, 'And how, pray tell, did the Harcourts come to know of the existence of such a boy, for surely London is full of urchins?' He smiled warmly at Lady Harcourt, who was dabbing a crocodile tear from her eyes with a lace handkerchief. 'I mean no disrespect to you, Lady Harcourt, by making this enquiry, for it is clear to all that you are a woman who is beyond reproach.'

The prosecution swept his arm back, with great flourish. 'If it may please the court, I would like to invite Lady Dorothy Harcourt to take the witness stand to explain how she was able to extend such an extraordinary kindness to a slum child. And to then have that same child ripped from the bosom of her family by this most wicked thief, in a most distressing and premeditated manner.'

'By all means,' said the judge, gazing at her in admiration.

She wafted across to the witness box and was sworn in, laying her hand upon the Bible, and then she began to tell her version of events: how she'd come to the Seven Dials to research her artistic project and plucked me from the slums, blessed me with money and tried to help me in every possible way, while I was just an ungrateful, scheming wretch.

'We had always wished for a son,' she said, beaming at her husband, who was examining the floor, 'but sadly this was not to be, and so when we were able to feed, clothe and play with little Jeremy at our home, offering him all our love and kindness, and we saw how he blossomed in our care, away from the deprivation and the loose morals of his family, it wasn't long before we both felt that it was our public duty to save him and to get him from this wayward slum girl and her pernicious influence. For she was acting as a mother to him in almost every aspect of his daily life because his mother, a laundress, was often incapable due to drink, and the lure of gin in particular.'

There were murmurs of appreciation from the public gallery at that, particularly among the starched collar brigade, who were doubtless better acquainted with slum girls after a night out at the theatre or the gentlemen's clubs than they'd ever admit to their sour-faced, prissy wives.

She was warming to her theme now, her violet eyes almost sparkling with malice. 'The more I saw of Mary Carr, the more I realised she was not a fit person to be involved in his care. She was polluting his young mind with her common vices.'

She wagged a finger at me. 'She started to put on airs and graces, she got above her station, using the money I had so kindly provided to pay her for her time spent posing for me as an artist's model, for my little project, a book of pictures entitled *London's Ragamuffins*. It was not without risk to myself that I entered the slums, but little did I know that I'd face such adversity, in the pursuit of my art.

'I felt so foolish, taking her under my wing like that, only for her to repay my kindness with the most revolting betrayal.'

The judge had been listening, with his head resting in his hand, but he perked up at the mention of a betrayal. He raised an eyebrow. 'Do go on, Lady Harcourt. I need the full facts if I am to deliver a verdict on this most distressing case.'

People were craning their necks, perching on the edge of their seats, to catch every word of the lies that just kept falling from her lips.

'One day, I was unwell and I had to remain in my boudoir rather than meet her for our regular artistic session. Seizing this opportunity, Mary Carr took it upon herself to suggest to my husband, the renowed artist Lord Harcourt, that she should sit for him, that she was to be his muse. He was bewitched by her, by her wicked flirtations.'

The assembled press bench, full of reporters, started scratching frantically in their notebooks, taking down every word of her bitter lies.

'Do go on,' said the judge.

'As part of my artistic endeavours, it was customary for her to dress in revealing clothing, the kind of clothing worn by slum girls in their daily lives, and she used this to her advantage, to entice my poor, dear husband.

'Heaven knows what wicked spells she wove upon him,' she said. 'She persuaded him to loan her my finest diamonds to wear for a portrait and he was mesmerised by her.'

Lord Harcourt buried his head in his hands.

'He painted her, just as she had instructed, as the Queen of Diamonds, wearing my jewels and even my slippers. The portrait was unveiled at the Royal Academy and much admired. Oh, how she relished that! And how she taunted me about it, revelling in the glory of being feted by so many when the portrait went on show. She grew proud and demanded – yes, demanded! – payment in the form of a diamond ring from my husband! He has only lately been able to make clear to me how he was foolishly ensnared by this minx, this drab from the slums. Due to his generous and artistic nature, he fell victim to her scheming.'

There were gasps of shock and horror and Lady Harcourt put her hand to her forehead and closed her eyes for a moment.

'My dear Lady Harcourt, I can imagine this must be most distressing for you to recount,' said the judge. 'Do you need to sit down for a moment to regain your composure?'

The clerk rushed over to give her a glass of water and she took a tiny sip as the rest of the court shot pitying glances in her direction. Lord Harcourt stared straight ahead, a muscle twitching in his cheek, but he made no attempt to tell the truth about me and him; how he had pursued me to pose for him in secret, for starters.

The judge looked down at him, and he shrank, fidgeting under his watchful gaze, as if he were tainted by guilt because of his association with me. I couldn't help noticing a few of his artistic chums were also looking very shifty and were doubtless counting their lucky stars that it wasn't their wife in the witness box pouring scorn on their dubious artistic liaisons with other girls from the London slums. Because they knew, as well as everyone in that courtroom, that all artists used girls from the lower classes for their portraits, and more besides. We were prepared to stand semi-naked for hours for whatever coins they'd press into our palms, and they loved us for it. It went without saying they did whatever took their fancy with us.

'I must continue,' she said, 'because this should serve as a warning to all who enter the den of thieves that is the Seven Dials and other areas of ill repute. We may be driven by the need to offer these urchin girls our charity, but they will always, always bite the hand that feeds them. This wicked girl cast a spell on my husband and then, even when she was gifted a diamond, this was not enough. She was determined to prevent us from helping her brother. It is against morality and human kindness; it is against everything that we stand for. We decided we had a duty

215

to care for such a vulnerable boy, to welcome him into our home and offer him all the love and kindness he could never experience with Mary Carr. Yet she conspired to prevent this, like the selfish wretch that she is.'

I felt anger rising in the pit of my stomach, it was like volcano about to erupt. I balled my hands into fists and clenched my jaw.

Still, she continued. 'Look at her,' she mocked, pointing a finger at me. 'Look at this girl and tell me she belongs anywhere other than the gutter.' A ripple of laughter crossed the benches.

'The very notion that she'd be able to care for a flea, let alone a child, is just ridiculous! But more than this, I fear she had a wicked plan, an evil scheme in mind, to blackmail us into handing over more diamonds, more money, in return for her not harming our little Jeremy!'

That was it. I could put up with her laughing at me, calling me names and being scornful of my poverty. I'd even accept her telling lies about how it was between Lord Harcourt and me, because he'd probably told her all sorts to cover up what he'd done. But suggesting that I'd use my little brother to blackmail her was a bridge too far. The rest of the court faded from view and all that was left was me and her, like two women facing off against each other on the cobbles, with scores to settle.

Before she had time to draw breath, I let out a shriek of rage and leaped out of the dock and charged across the courtroom, screaming 'Liar!'

The clerk and ushers made a grab for me, but I swatted them away like flies, as I sprang at her. She shrank from my grasp, but I sank my nails into her face, just as she'd stuck the knife into my portrait, and scratched like a wild animal until I drew blood.

'Help me!' she shrieked, as I dug at the flesh of her cheeks, howling at her, 'You lying bitch!'

It probably lasted only seconds, but it felt like time had stopped as I caught the look of terror in those violet eyes and felt the softness of her lily-white skin beneath my nails. Suddenly I was yanked backwards by my hair, still kicking and frothing with rage, away from Lady Harcourt, who let out a scream of agony and then fainted. Lord Harcourt rushed to her side, and she lay in his arms, whimpering and moaning, her hands covering her face, as blood seeped onto her white lace blouse.

'Restrain the prisoner!' roared the judge.

I was manhandled back to the dock and my arms were pinioned behind my back by two cozzers, who held onto me with a vice-like grip.

'She's a flaming liar! None of it's true . . .' But I didn't finish the sentence because one of the cozzers dealt me such a stinging blow to my mouth that my teeth rattled in my head and my lips swelled like a balloon. The court was in total uproar with people baying for my blood. I swear I heard someone scream, 'Hang her!'

The judge bashed his gavel again.

'The prisoner is deranged. She is morally and mentally defective as demonstrated by this appalling assault and outburst and the facts of this case as outlined by poor dear Lady Harcourt, who has now fallen victim to the most heinous and deplorable attack. I have no option in these circumstances other than to order her immediate and indefinite detainment.

'Mary Carr, there is only one place fit for you, where you will have time to reflect upon your sins and your wayward behaviour at length and that is Bethlehem Lunatic Asylum in South London.

'Take her away.'

CHAPTER 21

MARY
Bedlam, March 1900

They wrestled me into a strait jacket of thick heavy canvas, which was wrapped tightly around me, buckled at the back with leather straps, pinning my arms across my chest. My ankles were bound to stop me kicking and flailing and I was carried between two burly cozzers, like a sack, and slung into the back of the prison wagon while people watched, agape. Bethlehem Lunatic Asylum – Bedlam – was the place we were all warned about as kids in the Seven Dials. Exasperated mothers would shout at their kids, as they ran pell-mell down the lane, 'Oh, behave yourself or you'll end up in Bedlam!' Women who screeched at their husbands were told they belonged in there too. It was a place of nightmares.

Now it was my home, my prison, my world. I wasn't mad, just full of rage at what Lady Harcourt had done to me and full of fear at what she might do to Jem, a poor, innocent, trusting child. But in the eyes of the law, I was a raving lunatic, and from the moment I set foot in that asylum, with its domed roof and its neatly tended gardens, bordered by high, iron railings, I was told I was insane, wicked and I had to repent. And after a while and after what they did to me, amid the endless cries and howls of other inmates, I began to lose sight of Mary Carr, the resourceful and daring Queen of Diamonds from the Seven Dials. Bedlam was the beginning of the end of me.

I was carried from the police wagon and plonked on a wooden bench inside a cavernous entrance hall, where I was greeted by a welcoming party, if that's the right word, led by a bearded gent, dressed in a fine woollen suit, with a gold fob watch dangling from the pocket of his waistcoat. He was short, with heavy-lidded eyes and bulbous nose, and he reminded me of a gnome. He spoke in clipped tones. 'I am Dr Drew, the superintendent of this asylum. Mary Carr, you are admitted here at Her Majesty's Pleasure, as you are morally and criminally defective. You are entrusted to my care, and that of my staff, who you will treat with respect. Do you understand?'

I rolled my eyes and spat at his feet in disgust. I wasn't going to make it easy for them.

'I see you have much to learn. We will begin with a medical examination and then I will prescribe the best treatment for you,' he said, stroking his beard thoughtfully.

'It ain't wrong to want to be with my own brother!' I said. 'You can't keep me locked up for that.'

'I feel a period of quiet reflection may be in order,' he replied, smiling to himself, as he looked at the blob of spittle that had fallen dangerously close to his highly polished shoes. 'We are a caring community but you must accept that due to your mental and moral dereliction, you are no longer best placed to decide what is right for you. It is not a case of punishing you, it is a case of re-educating you, Mary, and helping you improve your mental and moral outlook. Reform, re-educate, repent, those are our watchwords.'

He went on, his voice echoing around the entrance hall. 'Ladylike values we expect from our inmates are piety, politeness, gratitude and service to others.'

A woman stepped forward, and at either side of her were two fearsome-looking fellas, who reminded me of the navvies I used to see working on building sites around the city. One of them bent down and untied my ankles, while the other kept tight hold of me. They both looked like they wanted to knock seven bells out of me, never mind improve my outlook.

'These are some of our attendants, who are here to assist as and when we need them. Please comply with their requests.' He afforded me a little smile at that, as if I had a choice. 'And this is Miss Comfort, our matron, who oversees all aspects of daily life for our female inmates, down to the last detail.'

If ever someone was misnamed at birth, it was her. She had a sarcastic sneer etched on her features, as if she just couldn't wait to dish up whatever was headed my way, because in her eyes I deserved it, and more.

'Come along!' she snapped, as I was marched away between her two bully-boys, down the corridor. Two more women were waiting for me in a room that was bare apart from a chair and a cotton nightgown, laid neatly across it. They were both wearing white blouses and navy woollen skirts, with thick leather belts and bunches of keys at their waists. Their hair was scraped back, and their faces had that same scornful, superior look as the matron.

'I will remove the strait jacket and you will undress,' said Miss Comfort. 'And if you don't behave yourself, we will see that you do and it will not be comfortable for you. Do you understand?'

I knew when I was outnumbered. I nodded.

'Take everything off,' she ordered, 'and put on the gown.'

She watched as I stripped down to my underwear. I unlaced my corset, blushing crimson, covering my bosom instinctively.

'You have no secrets from anyone in here, Mary,' she laughed, 'so don't be shy.'

Dr Drew walked in a few moments later, while Miss Comfort and her cronies hovered close by. He peered at my eyes, in my ears, down my throat and listened to my chest.

Then he lifted my gown, his eyes lingering for a moment on the little mound of hair between my legs, before he laid his hands upon my belly.

'Well, well,' he said, looking as if he'd lost a penny and found a pound. 'I do believe she is with child!'

Matron gasped.

'A fallen woman, indeed! How far along are you, Mary?' he said, putting his gnomish features so close to mine that I could smell the corned beef he'd had for his lunch.

'I ain't certain.'

Matron grabbed my arm and pinched the flesh, twisting it so that it burned. 'You will address the superintendent as "sir"!' she hissed. 'And you will tell the truth, girl.'

Tears sprang to my eyes. It hurt like hell.

'I think it's three months, sir,' I gasped, 'but I can't be sure.'

'I expect a slum girl could have any number of opportunities to end up in this kind of trouble, so I mustn't be too hard on you, given your moral insanity,' he said, stroking his beard. 'But I think a couple of month's solitary confinement is a good place to start.'

He turned to the matron. 'And we need to ensure she eats properly. I want that child born healthy.'

★

221

I was marched off down a maze of corridors, past rows and rows of locked, barred doors, as the cries of the poor unfortunate inmates filled my ears. There was singing and whining, howling and weeping, punctuated by high-pitched laughter and squealing. I wanted to block it out, but the attendants had taken hold of my arms, holding them firmly by my side. My feet were bare, growing colder on the flagstones, as I was dragged along, down to the basement.

Eventually, we stopped in front of a cell with an open door. It was six feet long and six feet wide – I know because I would go on to pace it out so often – with whitewashed walls, a wooden bench fixed to the floor and a thin mattress, covered by a blanket. The barred window was high overhead, with a small patch of sky just visible. A gown of thick, brown flannel lay on top of the mattress along with a pair of long, woollen stockings, which had been expertly darned, and a pair of scratchy cotton drawers.

'Put it all on,' said Miss Comfort. 'We don't want you catching your death of cold. You have baby to think about now.'

I did as she asked. The shapeless garment hung to my knees but at least it would go some way to keeping out the biting chill. She made me stand while the warders pulled and yanked at my hair, stitching it into a plait.

'That'll stop the tangles,' she laughed. 'You look like you belong in here now.'

'What about my things?' I said, tears pricking my eyes.

'We have those, nice and safe,' she said matter-of-factly. 'Everything is listed and kept under lock and key; everyone and everything. That is the way of the asylum.'

The door clanged shut. I sat down with my head in my hands and began to cry. But as I soon discovered, I was never left alone for long. Every now and then, the observation hatch on the door was pulled back and I'd catch a glimpse of someone spying on me. My food was delivered through that hatch three times a day, cut up small, like you'd give a child, and served in a metal dish with a spoon. I suppose I should have been grateful because I was given extra milk, extra meat, but I felt like I was a pig being fattened up for the market.

Once a day, for one hour, I was taken out, put in a leather body-belt with my arms chained to my sides, and marched around the gardens outside for exercise. I'd catch sight of other women, dressed in the same shapeless gowns as me, weeding, planting, digging in the vegetable patches and the flower beds. Some were doddery and shuffling, bent double, with hair as white as snow. An attendant either side of me made sure I couldn't stop and chat to anyone. Once a week, I was taken to be inspected by Dr Drew, who took huge pleasure in stroking, prodding and musing over my swelling belly.

'Oh yes, this child will be a good weight, a fine strapping, healthy baby,' he'd smirk, as Miss Comfort looked on approvingly. 'Is she eating well?'

'Yes, Dr Drew.'

Nobody asked for my opinion.

Sometimes I'd yell and scream in my cell, my voice mingling with the dreadful din made by the other poor sods in Bedlam, especially the ones down in solitary confinement like me.

Miss Comfort would rattle my cell door when I did that. 'Quieten down, Mary, or you'll be in here for even longer, I can assure you.' I had no control over anything and I was terrified about the baby, what would become of it, what would happen during the birth. After a few weeks, I realised that crying out was useless and that's when I started hearing another voice. It was a quiet voice, a girl, who spoke to me of the good times she'd had with her baby brother up in the Seven Dials; how she'd cared for him and loved him through the bad times and the good. I whispered his name to the spiders who came creeping from the gloomiest corners of my cell, swearing them to secrecy. If the matron or her warders heard me, I'd be punished, I was sure of it. I talked to the girl as often as I could, but her voice was so faint, so far away, sometimes I had to strain to hear it above the din from the other cells. And I only dared to mutter my replies, mumbling into my chest, my head bowed, in case anyone was watching.

You see, I didn't want them to know about my friend, the girl who was speaking to me, because I was supposed to be all alone, without anyone to talk to – that's what Dr Drew had said. Dr Drew, Miss Comfort and their evil helpers would find a way to stop her visiting, if they found out. So, I had to keep this secret from my keepers. My body was no longer my own and I feared I was losing my mind. I confided my worst fears to my secret friend, and she told me not to worry because she was there for me, and they'd never lock her up or catch her. She was wily and strong, clever and brave; she couldn't be caged, and she would never be silenced.

After two months in solitary confinement, when I was huddled in the corner where the spiders were, sharing my stories with them and listening out for my friend, the door to my cell swung open and I was hauled to my feet.

Dr Drew stood before me. 'I fear you are suffering from melancholia,' he said, peering at me. 'You are listless and quiet, too quiet for my liking, although I hear you have been murmuring to yourself, haven't you?'

Did he know my secret?

I was gripped by fear. I bit my lip and stared at the floor.

I heard the Whispering Girl beside me, in that very room. 'Don't breathe a word of it! Don't tell him!' Her voice was louder than ever. 'I'll never leave you but you can never tell.'

He gazed at me for a moment and then turned to Miss Comfort. 'Let's see if we can lift her spirits.'

I was seized by the warders and before I knew what was happening, I was marched down to the bathrooms, where a cast-iron tub full of water was waiting for me. They stripped me, and Dr Drew's eyes travelled over every inch of my pregnant body, my swollen breasts, my bulging belly, before they forced me into the freezing cold water.

I screamed in shock.

'Oh yes!' he cried, clapping his hands. 'This will awaken the nervous system and improve your mood. I have seen it so many times before. Ice cold baths once a day for a week, Miss Comfort, and send her to work in the laundry. Not near the ironing room, or the vats, but start her in the packing section, with the other melancholia patients.'

I was lifted from the bath wrapped in a sheet, dried roughly, and sent off, shivering in my brown gown, to work.

All the linen from the asylum, including the men's wards, was done in the laundry, and they made money out of us by taking in more from the factories and shops nearby, so there was a never-ending supply of clothing and bedding to be washed, dried, aired and pressed.

We had to put a long white apron over our gowns and wear the most ridiculous frilly mop caps. We were supposed to work in silence, but I learned to talk in a low voice, out of the corner of my mouth when the attendants weren't watching. I got to know a woman who'd been sent away like me, for criminal insanity, because she'd tried to strangle herself with her own stockings after bashing her husband around the head with a rolling pin. He'd survived but she couldn't face life as a mother of five with a no-good bloke who wanted to spend all his money on drink. I couldn't blame her for it, but the courts said she was morally insane.

There were several others who'd been carted off on the word of their husbands, because they were past child-bearing and feeling listless. One poor cow had taken to wearing a fancy bonnet and jackets cut for women in the first flush of youth and that had made her look so ridiculous that her doctors said she'd lost her mind. Her husband was busy getting his leg over with a younger woman anyway. Once she was inside these walls, it didn't take long for her to lose what was left of her sanity.

The company of others was a tonic to me, but nothing got in the way of my friendship with the Whispering Girl, who was my constant companion and my one true friend throughout the dark and lonely Bedlam nights, when I was locked in my cell, and haunted by the memories of the boy who had been stolen from me.

She warned me then that feeling love for him, longing for him, was weakness.

'You have to be hard, like a diamond, Mary,' she said. 'That's the only way you'll survive this.'

And the worst thing was, as she spoke to me in hushed tones, so that the warders wouldn't hear, I knew I could never get him back.

CHAPTER 22

Mary

Bedlam, August 1900

In the eighth month of my pregnancy, they moved me to a cell in another wing of the asylum, a place which I thought was paradise after the dank basement. Women sat on chairs in a line along the corridor, quietly getting on with their needlework and mending. They didn't speak much, if at all, but Miss Comfort liked it that way and so did Dr Drew, who took great pleasure in parading up and down, telling them, 'Well done, my dears. Such good work. You are a credit to the Bethlehem Asylum.'

If they had any bad thoughts about him, they kept them to themselves, probably out of the fear that they'd get sent back to solitary confinement for weeks on end. They wore the same brown gown as I did, but they were allowed a special item, something they'd made themselves – a pretty bonnet, an embroidered collar, a brooch with trimmings – something to distinguish them from the other inmates. Their hair was brushed and dressed with ribbons and bows, not stitched into a tight plait. Each had a basketful of sewing to get on with, and they worked from dawn until dusk, only breaking for lunch, tea and exercise. At the end of the corridor was a bird in a brass cage, which twittered on its perch. There were no anguished shouts or cries, only the sweet sound of a caged bird singing.

'You'll be housed here for the birth,' said Miss Comfort, showing me to a cell which was bigger and less gloomy than the one in the basement. 'And you can make yourself useful with the other women, bringing them threads, packing their piecework, until afterwards, when you'll be put to work as Dr Drew sees fit.'

'Please, Miss,' I said, even though I knew I risked punishment just for speaking without being asked to. 'I'm a seamstress, or at least, I was. I'm very good at sewing. May I try?'

'Needles are only given to our most trusted patients,' scoffed Miss Comfort.

But Dr Drew had been lurking behind the door, and he stepped forward.

'She could be given a test,' said Dr Drew, eyeing me closely. 'Some samples of work to mend and some sewing. Good seamstresses, skilled women, are hard to find, as you know, Miss Comfort.'

He approached me and cupped my face in his hands. 'I knew you would be special, Mary, when you came here and perhaps you are responding to the treatment we offer rather better than I'd hoped? Are you willing to work harder than you have ever worked to please me, to prove to me that you can do this?'

I nodded. Just being close to him made my flesh creep but I just wanted to get out of the laundry, particularly because I knew the misery of the women who spent their days heaving sheets and blankets in and out of those vast tubs, or pounding dirty linen at the scrubbing boards, until their hands were red-raw.

'But I must warn you, if you let me down, the consequences will be severe,' he said, with a glint in his eye.

★

That day I took up my needlework, fumbling a little at first. The fine threads I held were so fragile that I felt clumsy, but before long, I was caught up in my work, creating neat stitches, listening to the sweet twittering of the linnet in its cage.

My secret friend stood beside me, whispering her thoughts, but I knew I could not answer or make a sound. The peace and quiet was broken only by the squeaking of the warders' leather shoes as they kept watch.

Miss Comfort inspected some of my work and a smile played on her lips.

'Very good, Mary, you are a fine seamstress indeed! Dr Drew will be most pleased.'

After a week's work, I was rewarded with a linen bonnet to decorate, so that I could have a keepsake like the other needleworkers. When the ladies from the church came to visit, as they did on Sundays, with gifts of linen, threads, lace, ribbons and buttons, Dr Drew loved nothing more than to show off the work of his tamest, most dutiful inmates.

'See how we are rehabilitating these poor, troubled souls and helping them do something useful!' he'd murmur. 'Aren't they the very picture of womanhood?'

We were gazed upon with a mixture of pity and fascination as we perched on chairs outside our cells, heads bowed, sewing. It was on one of those Sundays, not long after I got the bonnet, that we received a gift of a button box to decorate our keepsakes. I opened it, catching my breath as I saw the delicate sheen of the mother-of-pearl buttons lying there. I picked one up and it caught the light, igniting the memories of my lost baby brother, and his first ever word, spoken in Mayfair and the afternoons he'd spent playing while I posed for Lady Harcourt.

Miss Comfort noticed and strolled over to me. 'What's wrong, Mary?'

'Don't say his name!' said the Whispering Girl beside me. 'They'll take it all away from you and throw you back in the basement. Keep quiet!'

'Nothing, thank you, Miss,' I murmured. 'It's just they're so beautiful. I'd like to sew some on my bonnet, if I may?'

She gazed down at me, giving a self-satisfied smile. 'That will be very pretty, Mary. You've come so far. Good girl.'

I picked up my needle and thread and began to stitch, first one button, then the other, until I had a whole row of them around the brim. Every time I sewed, I thought of Jem, swishing the buttons from the toy box in Mayfair, his face alive with delight, his laughter ringing out. Those buttons were a bridge between the past, a past I'd shared with him, and my lonely present locked up in here.

The others were jealous of my skills because I was able to make patterns that covered every inch of my bonnet. I could tell by the sideways glances they shot me. When I'd finished my work for the day, which was always twice as much as everyone else's, I was allowed to take my button box back into my cell before lights-out. The church ladies brought me things to put more buttons on – old jackets, and an old skirt, and sometimes I'd create pictures which they sold in the church to help the poor. As I sewed, the baby inside me kicked and wriggled and I grew so big that my back ached, and my belly strained against the scratchy brown flannel of my gown.

After weeks in that new wing, I was busy working on some button embroidery in my cell when my stomach went rigid, leaving me gasping for breath. I struggled to the door, hammering with my fists. 'Help me! Help me, I'm dying.'

The door swung open, just as a gush of water cascaded down my legs, which buckled beneath me. I doubled over in agony, clutching my belly.

'Oh, you silly girl,' said Miss Comfort, helping me to the bed. 'You're not dying. You're having the baby.'

'Push!' she commanded, as I clutched the iron bedstead, rivulets of sweat running down my forehead. An attendant stood behind her, with a pail of hot water and a bundle of towels.

I let out a wail, like an injured beast, and Miss Comfort tutted at me. 'Stop fussing. Women have been giving birth since the days of our good Lord Jesus, and they didn't see fit to make this kind of a racket. Keep still and let me have a look at you.'

The nightgown was wrenched up and she felt between my thighs, her fingers probing my most secret places. 'Yes, the head is there, you need to push again when I tell you. But not before, or you'll tear yourself to pieces.'

The pain came in waves; I just wanted it to stop. I thrashed my head from side to side, the cell walls blurring before me. I gave a huge push when she told me to and the pressure eased as something was pulled from me, bloody, wriggling, and then it let out a cry.

My baby was born.

I opened my eyes to see it, all covered in blood, with a mop of black hair, eyes tightly shut, like a kitten. Miss Comfort lifted her up and inspected her, peering at every inch of her, before saying, 'It's a girl. She's perfect, except for the red birthmark on her thigh, but nobody will worry about that.' She wrapped her in a towel and pulled out a set of scissors, snipping the cord that joined us.

I stretched out my hands to hold my baby, to bring her to my breast.

'Please,' I said, 'can I feed her?'

The two women exchanged glances.

'Very well,' said Miss Comfort, 'just this once.'

They thrust her towards me, and I cradled her in my arms, as she fed. I stroked her cheek, feeling the softness of it, her newborn, perfect skin warm against my own. In that moment, she opened her eyes and we gazed at each other. She was every bit as beautiful as my baby brother, but I'd made her; through the nightmare of Bedlam, I'd created this gorgeous little scrap of humanity.

My head was spinning. I heard the Whispering Girl say, 'She's yours, Mary. Nothing can change that. But remember, to love is to be weak.' I bit my lip, so that I couldn't reply because then Miss Comfort would know I'd been keeping a secret from her. I began to hum a lullaby instead. Then, when the baby was sleeping soundly in my arms, her tiny fingers curled around my own, Miss Comfort snatched her away and wrapped her in a fresh towel.

'Can't she stay a little longer?' I said meekly, feeling a pull of longing for my infant.

'Don't be silly, girl,' scoffed Miss Comfort, handing the sleeping bundle to her assistant, 'Dr Drew has plans for her. You are not fit to raise a baby. The very thought of it!'

I felt bitter tears spring to my eyes, try as I might to contain them. 'Please, wait!' I said, but I was so weak, I couldn't stand. I was powerless to stop her leaving.

And the door to my cell was already closing.

My breasts ached with the milk I wasn't allowed to feed her, swelling painfully and my gown was soaked through by the morning. When my cell door opened at first light,

Miss Comfort brought strips of linen and tied them around my chest, binding them tightly. 'This will stop the flow in a few days' time,' she said. 'It's for the best.'

'But can't I feed her myself?'

She shook her head. 'No, Mary. You can't because she isn't yours to keep. Don't ask silly questions again, or I will have to talk to Dr Drew about you. Do you understand?'

I nodded obediently.

'Now, get up, and come to the bathrooms to clean yourself up, and then there's work to do after breakfast.'

I shuffled painfully along the corridor, joining the line of dutiful inmates, who did exactly what they were told, stripping off their drawers and washing, while my whole body ached with unspoken longing for the little girl I'd given birth to, but who I wasn't allowed to see. There were a few pitying glances from the others as we stood at the washstands, but nobody breathed a word of the birth or the baby, although they must have heard me crying out. The rest of the week passed in a blur of endless needlework, but I didn't sew buttons in the evenings as I usually would, preferring to lie in my cell, with my face to the wall, listening for the whispered kindnesses from my secret friend, who knew exactly how lonely I was feeling, because she felt it too.

A week later, when I'd given up all hope of seeing my child again, Miss Comfort bustled down the corridor as I was busy mending a dress. 'Come along, Mary,' she said, clapping her hands, 'Dr Drew will see you in his office now.'

I knew better than to question why, but I began to fear that my listless behaviour had come to his attention and started to quake at the thought of what new treatment he'd prescribe to cure it. Miss Comfort had warders with her, who followed close behind me, as we climbed the flagstone staircase to a part of the asylum I'd never seen before. The walls were panelled with oak and the parquet floor was waxed and shiny. We stopped in front of a door, and she knocked softly before entering.

Dr Drew was there, sitting in a green leather-backed chair, behind the most enormous desk covered with papers. A warder was beside him, with a baby wrapped in a bundle of blankets in her arms. I caught a glimpse of her pink face, the curls of her hair, and she was sleeping like an angel. My stomach lurched. 'My baby,' I whispered.

I'd barely uttered those words before the two assistants had grabbed my arms, pinning them to my side.

'Ah yes, here is Mary now,' said Dr Drew, to a couple who had their backs to me and were perched on chairs in front of him.

The man looked me up and down, as if he were sizing up an animal at the farmer's market. 'She's a good-looking thing for a lunatic, isn't she?' he said, addressing his comments to Dr Drew. 'Do you think her mental weakness will be inherited by the child, because we want to offer this little mite a home, but we don't want any trouble. I need a good worker, no nonsense.'

His wife, who had a pinched expression, wore her hair in tight ringlets, which shook every time she nodded her head in agreement with her husband.

'The child has a red birthmark on her leg but is otherwise a perfect specimen,' said Dr Drew. 'There were no problems with the delivery. The mother is clean, no diseases, and there is no reason to think, with a firm and guiding hand through life, that this child will disappoint you in any way.'

I clenched my fists and the warders responded to the tension coursing through my body, by tightening their grip on me. How could they discuss my baby as if it were something to be bought and sold in a shop?

'No!' I gasped. 'It ain't right! Please Dr Drew, please don't send my baby home with these strangers.'

'Enough!' said Dr Drew, slamming his hands down on the desk. 'How dare you question the integrity of this fine, upstanding couple. They have a very good trade as tailors over in the East End, and they are willing to offer the child of your sinful union a decent and loving home. How dare you question my judgement!'

'We've decided to name her Catherine, after my mother,' said the wife primly, ignoring the tears of anguish rolling down my cheeks. 'Kate for short.'

'But I wanted to call her Polly,' I said, 'after a friend I had in the Seven Dials.'

'You'll have no say in the matter,' Dr Drew cut in. 'Her future is decided, and you can play no part in it.' He produced an ink pen from the pot on his desk. Then, he picked up a sheaf of papers and pulled out the bottom one, turning it around so that it faced my side of the desk. 'All that remains is for you to sign here, to say that you agree the legal adoption order.'

I shook my head. 'No, I won't do it. You can't force me.'

Miss Comfort took that as her cue to signal to her two assistants to drag me, bodily, to the edge of that desk. I started to struggle but they held me still while she grabbed hold of my hand, placed the pen in my fingers, and closed her own hand around it, pushing it down onto the paper.

'You will sign and you will be very sorry that you've caused all this upset, Mary,' she grimaced, her eyes almost bulging out of their sockets with the effort of steadying me. Dr Drew sat back in his chair, and stroked his beard. 'I can see we need to take a much firmer line with you, Mary.

It seems you have been spoiled by me of late, indulged even. It's not been good for your mental state, clearly. You have become disruptive and difficult.'

I started to kick and flail, until one of the warders sank to her knees and grabbed my legs. The pen was hovering over the paper. Inch by inch, Miss Comfort forced my hand downwards, scraping one line and then another, until it formed an X.

'I know how to write!' I screamed. 'That isn't my signature!'

But Dr Drew had snatched the paper away and he scribbled 'Her Mark' next to it.

'It seems you have forgotten how to write, Mary, because you have taken leave of your senses, and so this is the best that you could do. It's all perfectly acceptable and it's not unusual in the asylum.'

He stood up. 'Congratulations on becoming the proud parents of a baby girl.'

I lashed out wildly, biting, screaming, trying to kick myself free. The couple moved away swiftly, cowering at the side of the room, pressing themselves against the fancy flocked wallpaper, while Dr Drew called for assistance. A moment later, two male warders came charging through the office door with a strait jacket, as Miss Comfort and her cronies used all their might to force me to the floor. I was wrapped into that heavy canvas, my arms pinned at my side.

'It's the padded cell for you, my girl,' said Miss Comfort, hauling me to my feet. 'Let's see how you like that!'

'Come with me, please,' said Dr Drew to my daughter's new parents, ushering them out of the room. He presented them with the perfect little bundle. 'I think you've seen enough of her madness. I must apologise for her appalling behaviour.'

My baby let out a cry.

'Stop fussing!' said the wife sharply, making her cry even more.

'She'll always be my child!' I screamed.

But that was the last I saw of her.

CHAPTER 23

Mary
Bedlam, June 1916

'Stand up straight please, Mary.'

I was so used to being bent over my needlework all day that I struggled to do as the new superintendent of the asylum asked. There were no attendants holding my arms, just Miss Comfort, pursing her lips at me and looking disapproving.

Dr Henry Boothby had only been at Bedlam for a few months, but there was no mistaking the difference in the way he spoke to me, as if I were a human being, rather than some wild animal to be tamed. There was kindness in his eyes, and I'd never once heard him raise his voice or talk about reforming people who were confused, anguished and didn't know what day of the week it was.

He was flanked by two other men, one very elderly, with a bushy grey beard, and the other younger, but more serious-looking, with a pair of gold-rimmed glasses perched on the end of his nose. Before them on the desk were stacks of dun-coloured paper files, stuffed with papers. One was open in front of him.

Many years had passed since I came to this place, so many I'd lost count, and sometimes I even forgot my own name, preferring the nickname the warders gave me, Pearlie. I was known for my clothing adorned with buttons, the swirling and detailed patterns I'd stitch with them, as well as the pictures

I made for the church ladies to sell to their friends to raise money to buy sewing and embroidery supplies to amuse us.

They chattered amongst themselves on their Sunday visits, and it wasn't long before I'd learned that there was a war, a terrible war, which had claimed so many of their husbands, brothers and sons. And that war was the reason that my keeper and tormentor Dr Drew finally left Bedlam and Dr Boothby arrived. You see, Dr Drew was needed to help the men who'd lost their minds in battle, because of the noise of the guns and the dreadful sights they saw.

'It's a war like no other, but it'll soon be over,' said one woman. 'And Dr Drew has volunteered to deal with the poor souls suffering trench fever, to help them get back to the front.'

'I just wish the good Lord had seen fit to spare my boy,' said her friend. 'Even with trench fever, he'd still be alive.' She dabbed the corner of her eye with a lace handkerchief. 'Dr Boothby is a fitting replacement for Dr Drew. He already has the confidence of the staff.'

Well, that wasn't true. I'd seen Miss Comfort looking daggers at him when his back was turned. What's more, a few of the ladies on my wing had disappeared and nobody knew where they'd gone. There were whispered discussions about it in the bathrooms and on the way to chapel. And now, standing before Dr Boothby, my legs started tremble as I feared I may be next.

'Do you remember why you were sent here, Mary?' he began. The other two fellas had their ink pens poised, ready to start writing down my reply.

The words stuck in my throat. The Whispering Girl, who'd been my companion through so much behind these walls, told me, 'Don't tell 'em a bleeding thing, Mary, or they'll send you to solitary, like they always do.'

Dr Boothby smiled at me. 'Take your time, Mary.'

My voice was hoarse, cracking with emotion, and I spoke quietly because the only time I talked to other inmates, I had to be careful not to be caught.

'I did something wrong, a long time ago,' I began.

'Do you recall what that was?' said the bearded gent, resting his chin in his hands, gazing at me intently.

'Don't say it!' said the Whispering Girl.

'I don't think I'm supposed to remember it, sir,' I said. 'Or I'll be in trouble.'

The three of them exchanged glances.

'I can promise you that you won't be,' said Dr Boothby.

But Miss Comfort cut in. 'If you don't mind me saying so, doctor, we have never encouraged this patient to talk of her crime because Dr Drew always said it reinforced the behaviour and she'd focus her troubled mind . . .'

'Thank you, Miss Comfort,' said Dr Boothby stiffly. 'You may leave.'

She flushed bright red, like a beetroot. 'But that's not safe, Dr Boothby!' she said indignantly.

'I'll be the judge of that, Miss Comfort. And I believe this patient poses no further risk to herself or to anyone else. But I need her to be able to speak freely and I believe that your presence in this room may be preventing that.'

She turned on her heel and slammed the door shut behind her.

I swallowed and paused for a moment. The secrets I'd shared with the Whispering Girl every night were still fresh in my mind. Did I dare to share them now?

'I took something, someone, I shouldn't have done,' I began, even though I wasn't sure I felt I'd done wrong, because he was my own brother.

'Who was this person?' said the more serious of the three of them, glancing up from his notebook.

'Please, sir, it was my little brother, because I was upset and I wanted to be with him.'

'Do you know what year it is today, Mary?' said Dr Boothby.

I shook my head. 'I only know I like sewing my mother-of-pearl buttons that the church ladies bring every Sunday.'

They exchanged glances again.

'And do you accept, after all these years, that what you did was wrong, Mary?' Dr Boothby went on, 'That you should not have taken this child, even though he was your brother, because he'd been adopted lawfully. And you should never have attacked Lady Harcourt?'

The Whispering Girl was screaming beside me. 'Don't give in to them, she had it coming!'

I dug my nails into my palms, desperate to take my mind off what she was saying. 'I do know it was wrong, sir,' I said. 'Terribly, terribly wrong.' I didn't want to go to solitary, I didn't want to have the strait jacket and the ice baths. If I told them my true feelings, I knew I'd be in trouble.

'And do you promise never to try to see this family, the Harcourts, again? Because if you do, Mary, I can tell you, we will find out and we will have to keep you here for the rest of your days.'

'I promise,' I said. I was old before my time, greying, and my eyes were weak from all the sewing, and I didn't understand how to live without someone locking the door to my cell at night, to keep me safe and to prevent me from harming anyone. There was no fight left in me now. They muttered amongst themselves for a moment.

'There is also the matter of a child you bore, out of wedlock, who was also adopted by another family,' began Dr Boothby. I still cried for her sometimes in the dead of night, that perfect little girl, with her sweet face and cloud of dark hair so like her father's. My baby, Polly. Oh, the Whispering Girl gave me such a hard time for my weakness, telling me to forget her.

'Yes,' I said, feeling tears welling in my eyes, 'I remember that baby.'

'We'd also make it a condition of your release that you can never seek out that family. The child is theirs. Do you understand?'

Something about that made tears roll down my face before I could stop them.

Again, the Whispering Girl shrieked in my ear. 'I've told you this a thousand times. You can't feel any love for that child, she's long gone. Don't you dare cry about her, not now!'

I bit my lip, as I always did when I stopped myself from replying to her out loud. That could only happen when I was sure I was alone in my cell, with no one spying on me through the hatch, or I'd be banged up in the basement for weeks on end, dunked in cold baths or put on bread and water to tame me.

I took a deep breath, 'Yes, sir. I promise I will never try to find her.'

'Then, in that case Mary, once you have packed up your belongings, I will see to it that you are free to go. And your bonnet is very pretty indeed. You are a fine seamstress. I'm sure the other ladies will miss your considerable talents.'

I curtseyed. My head was spinning but a door to the outside world was opening, a chink of light was shining, and I knew, come what may, I was going to step through it.

CHAPTER 24

ALICE

Elephant and Castle, December 1925

I couldn't see the point of living.

As I stared down into the murky, swirling waters of the Thames from Waterloo Bridge, I thought of everything I'd stolen and everything that had been taken from me in this godforsaken city. My legs were heavy as lead, and I was sure if I jumped, I'd sink straight to the bottom, down into the mud, with all the other London rubbish.

The sun was going down, casting its red-orange glow onto the grand buildings lining the north side, which promised wealth and glory, while the south was a grimy mass of wharves, factories, tenements and the rotting timbers of water-licked jetties, where the lightermen stowed their barges and loaded cargo. It was also the place I'd called home for so long.

They say when a man's tired of London, he's tired of life. Nobody had ever thought of asking a woman's opinion on that, not as far as I knew, but I'd had enough of London. Or, perhaps, London had had enough of me?

I'd been released from Holloway that morning. Freedom felt like another prison sentence. I spent hours wandering aimlessly through the West End, looking at my old haunts, the shops, with a feeling of dread and shame at what I'd become. Babyface should have been here beside me, but

I'd left her buried in that shallow grave. I was a grass, a screw's nark, a liar and a coward who'd turned her back on friendship.

I didn't deserve my liberty because I'd condemned her to a miserable existence and a terrible death. The water was beckoning me now. My stomach heaved and lurched as I leaned further over, looking intently at the river below me, wondering how many other women had plunged over the edge to drown their sorrows.

It would only take a moment, then I'd feel the water's cold embrace and be done with it all. My hands gripped the smooth stone ledge as I prepared to launch myself headfirst over the bridge and into the River Thames. But something was tugging at the edge of my coat.

I looked down to see a dog, a white Bull Terrier, with a brindle splodge over its left eye, with its jaws clamped firmly around the hem of my fur. It was pulling me away, snarling and shaking its head from side to side, with such vigour that I thought it might tear a hole in it.

'Get off me!' I said, trying to shake it off. I'd worked hard to hoist that coat and even if I was going to end it all, I wasn't going to let some hound ruin it.

That's when I recognised it as Geezer, Pearlie's funny little dog, and I caught sight of her, rushing towards me over the bridge, in her full regalia of long skirt and jacket with its nipped-in waist, all covered in mother-of-pearl buttons and her hat with ostrich feathers in the top. She looked like she'd stepped out of the last century. But here she was.

'What the bleeding hell d'you think you're playing at, Alice Diamond!' she yelled, waving her arms at me. I'd never heard her raise her voice before, because if the truth be told, she often spoke in a bit of a whisper, especially when she was telling her stories about Mary Carr, the Queen of Thieves. 'Don't you dare go topping yourself!' she shouted. 'Don't you flaming dare.'

'Call your dog off!' I shouted back, as Geezer snarled at me.

She put her fingers in her mouth and gave a loud whistle, and he immediately let me go. His tail wagged, and he licked my hand with his drooly tongue as if we were best friends. Pearlie made her way towards me, strands of grey hair escaping from her hat, whipped by the wind, her eyes blazing with anger. 'What on earth do you think you're up to?' she said, breathlessly, clutching her chest from the effort of getting across the bridge.

I shrugged. A flush of embarrassment crept up under my collar that she'd caught me trying to end it all.

'Just looking at the river, I s'pose,' I lied. 'There was nothing more to it than that. It's been a long time since I saw it.'

'Oh, pull the other one, love, it's got bells on,' she said. She glared at me. 'I ain't finished telling you my story yet. I've waited two long years, and this is how you repay me?'

I couldn't help laughing at that. She had no clue about what I'd been through, what I'd done; she only cared about our stupid storytelling bargain. It was so ridiculous, I had to see the funny side, because God knew, there hadn't been much to laugh about in my life lately.

'What's your game?' she said crossly.

'Nothing,' I replied, suppressing a giggle.

She folded her arms across her chest as Geezer hung at her heels, wagging his stumpy tail. 'I heard a rumour that you'd be getting out of prison,' she went on, glancing around, 'but where's that other little chum of yours, the one who liked showing off her hoisted furs to all and sundry?'

I gazed up at the darkening sky, as the last rays of the sun disappeared behind the rooftops.

'She didn't make it out of Holloway,' I said, my voice cracking with emotion. 'She got sick . . .'

'I'm sorry for your loss,' said Pearlie briskly. 'But life goes on, Alice. And you made it, didn't you, and you're on a promise. To me, remember?'

She made it sound so simple, getting over the death of my friend. Before I had time to protest, she'd linked her arm through mine. 'Fancy a nice cup of tea?' And I was swept along on Pearlie's tide.

If you'd told me a couple of years ago that I'd be relying on the charity of Pearlie the flower seller, I'd have laughed in your face. Yet here I was, fresh out of prison, down in the dumps, and looking forward to a reviving brew at her place. I had no idea that Pearlie even had somewhere to doss down; I'd imagined her roughing it under a heap of blankets behind a barrow up some alleyway, huddling next to Geezer for warmth.

She steered me back over the bridge, down some steps and up a narrow side street, with railway arches on one side, and a tiny row of terraces on the other. All the houses shook every time a train went by overhead and the cobbled street was full of rubbish. The houses were filthy with soot and rats were scurrying about all over the place. Geezer ran to catch one.

We walked to the end of the row, stopping in front of a house with boarded-up windows and a battered wooden door with peeling paint. 'Welcome to my home,' she said, opening the door and shoving me inside before I had the chance to change my mind. The staircase had long since rotted, putting the upper floor out of bounds. I glanced at the bare boards in the front room as we walked down the hallway into the scullery.

'The rent man never bothers calling, which suits me just fine,' she said, before I had time to ask how much she was paying for the place. It was a miracle the walls were still standing because they were covered with a thick, black mould and bits of plaster had come down from the ceiling, exposing the thin lathe boards underneath.

She had few possessions: a rocking chair by the fireplace, an old iron bedframe covered with a tatty eiderdown and a blanket, a kettle and a pot for cooking on the range, a table and chair, a couple of bits of chipped china, and that was about all, other than a rusty pail by the sink. The dog had a basket in the corner. Oh, and there was a sewing box on the table with pearl buttons scattered all over it, heaps of them.

'Nice place you've got, Pearlie,' I said politely, as she sploshed water into the kettle and stuck it on the range to heat. She whistled to herself. It sounded like an off-key version of 'London Bridge is Falling Down'.

'Fanks,' she said. 'Take a pew. But don't you dare touch my buttons.'

'Wouldn't dream of it,' I replied.

I sat down on the rickety chair and prayed it wouldn't collapse under me, because it was mostly woodworm. The quarry tiled floor had once been red, I could tell, even though it was now covered with a thick layer of grime. I didn't particularly want to get better acquainted with it because the grease would never come off my fur coat.

'I see some of your other chums around the Elephant, from time to time, the girls you used to go shopping with,' she said, eyeing me closely. 'I expect they'll be pleased to catch up with you. Are you going to get your gang back together?' There was a glimmer of something approaching hope in her face as she spoke.

The question was like a knife through my heart. Suddenly, the river seemed preferable to answering it.

'I just need a bit of time to work out my next move,' I mumbled. 'It takes a while to readjust to everyday life, after you've been inside.'

'Lost your bottle, have you?'

I shook my head. I'd lost more than that, but I could never explain it. I'd lost my dearest friend, the woman I loved more than anyone else, my honour, my dignity and my nerve. Even the rats rooting through the rubbish outside were better than me.

The kettle started to whistle, as Geezer came trotting in and sat down at my feet, curling his body, so that I could feel his tail thumping against me.

'Well, he seems to like you,' she said, as Geezer got up and licked my fingers. I tried not to dwell on where he'd been putting his muzzle in that alleyway. 'And he's quite choosy, you know, about the company he keeps. He ain't bitten you, which is a good sign.'

She spooned some tea leaves into the pot and stirred it before sniffing at the opened bottle of milk beside the sink. Then, she brought it over to the table, setting down her chipped teacups.

'Can't say I get many visitors, so you'll have to take me as you find me, Alice,' she said, pouring me a brew.

It was scalding hot, and I blew on it, before taking a sip. That tea was so delicious after a day on my feet that I couldn't imagine anything better, even if I was just here, perching in this hovel with Pearlie.

'I was wondering,' I began, 'if I might stay for a few days, just until I find my feet and work out my next move?'

She took a sip of her tea.

'I s'pose it will give me the chance to tell you the rest of the story about Mary Carr, won't it?' she said. 'But I don't carry passengers, it's just me and Geezer. So you'll have to pay your way.'

I almost laughed at that – the idea that she was going to charge me rent for a few nights in this dosshouse, but the alternative was going back to Queen's Buildings to face the girls and I just couldn't, not yet.

'I'll get a job,' I replied.

The tallyman was pleased as Punch to see me the next morning, as he went on his rounds through the Elephant and Castle. I lurked in the alleyway near the market while he collected his dues from the housewives who owed him for his wares, then I caught up with him as he was clambering back up on to his cart.

'Well, well,' he said, recognising me, despite the fact that I had my hat pulled down low. 'How are the mighty fallen! Didn't you used to be the queen of something or other round these parts?' He hated my guts because of the way me and the girls had undercut him.

I shrugged.

'Life's full of ups and downs, ain't it?' I said, swallowing my pride and fighting the urge to punch him on the nose. 'I'm just looking for piecework, that's all, if you've got any?'

He acted as an unofficial go-between for the fur factories and the tailors, taking a cut of their profits too, the oily sod.

'Fur pulling?' he said, with an evil smile playing on his lips.

'I was hoping for some mending . . .' I began, but he cut me dead.

'Nope, the only thing I've got is a basketful of dead coneys making a terrible stink on the back of the wagon.

And there's more to come if you're interested? All my regular girls have already had the pick of the piecework, Alice, and you ain't even tried and tested, so I can't take the risk, see? It's the bunnies or nothing.'

Fur-pulling was honestly the world's worst profession, toiling for hours over baskets of dead rabbits, stripping their fur with a blunt knife, piling the stinking skins on one side to be sold to make coats, and the fluff on another, to go for coat-making or stuffing pillows, sofas and mattresses.

My fingers had grown strong from oakhum-picking, so I knew I could do it, but the task was thankless, and the fluff got everywhere, making you choke. The fur-pullers were the poorest, wheeziest bunch of women in London. But I didn't have many other options. I needed to earn something, even if it was a pittance, just to keep a roof over my head for the time being.

'I'll take the basket,' I said. 'And you can bring me another one in the morning. But I need to be paid by the day.'

'You reckon you can get through this lot in a day?'

He raised an eyebrow and pulled a wicker basket filled with furry carcasses from the back of his cart, plonking it down on the pavement. I picked it up.

'Let's see how you get on with that lot first and we can talk more after that,' he said smugly, tipping his cap at me as I heaved it onto my hip and walked away.

Fur-pulling was every bit as bloody awful as I'd feared, and when Pearlie came home she hit the roof about the fluff scattered over her filthy scullery. I tried my very best to keep it in the basket, but it got everywhere – mostly up my nose, it had to be said. I had to move the stripped skins off the floor sharpish too, before Geezer got hold of one. He sat at my feet, wagging his tail, expectantly.

'Bleeding hell, Alice,' said Pearlie, taking off her jacket, 'I ain't sure I can put up with this mess! Couldn't you have found a better job?' She went to open the window.

'No!' I said. 'If you do that the fluff might blow away, just let me bag it up first.'

I shoved fistfuls of the stuff into the sack at the bottom of the wicker basket and threw the skins on top, while she tutted at me. I didn't want all my hard work going to waste.

'I'm off to get more from the tallyman. I'll be back in a bit,' I said, standing up and stretching my legs because I'd got pins and needles. I'd been there for hours, and it was already getting dark outside, but I wanted to get another basket to earn some money, even if it meant working by candlelight.

'I was hoping to tell you the last bit of Mary's story,' said Pearlie. 'Don't be too long, will you? I've got a nice pie for you.' She unwrapped a juicy bone from some old newspaper and set it down in front of the hearth. Geezer trotted over and began to gnaw at it.

She looked a bit crestfallen that I was leaving. I'd spent ages listening to Mary Carr's tale last night. The poor cow had tried to rescue her brother from some posh family who'd adopted him to spite her, then she got banged up in Bedlam, which was a hellhole by all accounts, and she was pregnant with some toff's baby. Listening to it was a bit of a chore. I'd felt my eyes closing, heavy with sleep, as Pearlie droned on, but she'd kept prodding me to keep me awake. In the end, it was a mercy when she finally nodded off in the old armchair and I sneaked into that old iron bed for a bit of a kip.

'I'll come straight back,' I said, pulling on my coat. 'And thanks for the pie.'

'I'll wait for you,' she said, as I was leaving with the basket of skinned rabbits. 'We can eat together.'

As I was struggling to get that knackered old front door to shut behind me, I could have sworn I heard her muttering to herself. 'She ain't dangerous! Just shut up. It's my secret to tell. I ain't listening to you no more.'

The tallyman was loitering around the market, leaning on a lamppost and watching the world go by. He had long legs and a handsome face, with a cheeky grin, but there was something smug about him in the way that he tucked his thumbs into the thick leather belt around his waist. He looked like a fella who knew he'd got the whole community on the hook because that is what he was. He saw me approaching with my fur-pulling work, and he swaggered over to peer inside the basket.

'Well done,' he said, taking it from me, unable to hide his disappointment that I'd completed the work so quickly. 'You got through that lot in no time.' He put his hand in his pocket and gave me two shillings. Two measly shillings for all those hours of thankless toil! But I was in no position to argue. I snatched the coins from his grasp.

'I'll take another basket and get that back to you in the morning,' I said. 'Then you can give me another one for the evening.'

'Blimey,' he said. 'You're keen, aintcha? You'll be stuffing every mattress this side of the river if you keep that up. Did they teach you fur-pulling in Holloway?'

He smirked at his question, knowing that he was needling me with it.

I imagined him, tiny and insignificant, being crushed under the heel of my shoe.

'No, that was much tougher, actually,' I replied. 'There's a reason it was called hard labour. I ain't got all day, where's the next lot?'

He led me up the alleyway to his cart, where his old mare was munching on a nosebag full of oats. She was dutiful and blinkered, just like all the women who were conned by him, with his shoddy wares and ludicrous, inflated repayments. Looking at him, as he pulled another basketful of dead rabbits from the back of his cart, I began to recall the reason why I'd gone into the hoisting game, to be free of the need to work for arseholes like him.

It started as a sense of anger, twisting in my stomach, but then I remembered all the good times I'd had and that stopped me in my tracks because Babyface was in all of them; laughing as we scarpered out of Selfridges with our knickers full of loot, celebrating with the others after a hard day's shopping. All my best memories were of her.

'Wake up, Dolly Daydreams!' said the tallyman, as I stood there, staring into space.

I wasn't daydreaming, the idiot, I was living a nightmare.

I mumbled an apology and took the basket and made my way back to Pearlie's place before I was tempted to take one of those dead rabbits out of the basket and ram it down his throat. The hot-chestnut seller was still doing a brisk trade, as it was a freezing cold evening, and the lights were blazing up ahead in the pub on the corner. I was like a moth to a flame. The thought of a drink to warm me up and take my mind off my troubles suddenly seemed like a very good idea. God knows, I'd earned it because my throat was dry and scratchy from all the rabbit fluff, and I needed something to sustain me through another long evening listening to Pearlie chuntering on about Mary bleeding Carr.

I pushed the door open and squeezed through with my basket of dead rabbits. The rancid smell they gave off wasn't a problem, not in that smoke-filled dive of a pub. The newspaper seller was warming the cheeks of her backside by the fire, lifting her skirt, while a couple of old fellas looked on appreciatively, because she was known for not wearing knickers. The usual dice games were going on in the corner, and those who'd already lost their week's wages were staring hopelessly into their pints, wondering what they'd tell her indoors later.

The barman caught sight of me through his one good eye – he'd lost the other in a knife fight before the Great War. He always said that was a blessing rather than a curse, because all his chums who volunteered or got conscripted were blown to bits in the trenches within weeks of arriving in France.

'Brandy, please,' I said, slamming a shilling down on the bar. 'Make it a large one.'

'Alice, ain't it? Haven't seen you in a while. Shall I tell your mates, Bertha and Gert, you're back in the parish?'

'Don't bother,' I said as he poured me a drink.

He pushed the shilling back towards me. 'It's on the house. The first drink when you get out of the nick is always free in here.'

'Very kind,' I said, glugging the brandy, feeling it warming me, lightening my mood. I pushed the coin back towards him. 'I'll have another.'

'The missus was saying only the other day she'd quite like a new fur wrap for the winter,' he said, giving me a wink, 'if you know what I mean.' He refilled my glass, and I tipped that back swiftly because I didn't want to bump into Gert and Bertha, not yet; I just wasn't ready for it. Everything seemed brighter, warmer, more welcoming as the booze caught me in its warm embrace. I swilled the last dregs around my glass.

'I do know what you mean and I'm sure I can oblige,' I said, sipping the last drops of my drink. 'But it's a chilly night, ain't it? A good brandy makes things look so much rosier.'

He pushed the bottle towards me. 'Happy to oblige, if you can get me that fur in time for Christmas.' I picked up the bottle and laid it down on top of my rabbits. 'I'll be in touch,' I said, feeling the brandy glowing in the pit of my stomach as I made my way back out into the cold night air.

I wasn't sure I could keep my side of the bargain but I'd cross that bridge when I came to it.

Pearlie had lit an oil lamp and set the pies out on the table by the time I got back to her place. I tucked my bottle of brandy underneath the rabbits in case she spotted it. I didn't want her to start asking questions about why I'd taken so long with the tallyman. It wasn't that I was ashamed of wanting a drink after a hard day's graft, but it was my business, not hers. The booze had taken the edge off my appetite, but I was grateful for the supper all the same, and I tucked in hungrily.

'It's steak and kidney,' she said, licking her lips, as Geezer whined with longing, watching us with his beady little eyes. 'You'll be up for hours with that lot,' she went on, gesturing to the basket. 'But I'll keep you company and sew a few more buttons.' My heart sank. There was to be no escape from her endless storytelling.

When she'd finished, she wiped the crumbs from her mouth with the back of her hand and gave Geezer her plate to lick clean before taking up her sewing box and sitting down by the fire. I lifted my work basket onto the table and picked out one of the greasy skins and my fur-puller's blade. Then, I clamped the rabbit between my knees and stretched it with one hand before sweeping downwards with my knife to remove the fur, coughing as I did so.

Pearlie spoke in that low voice of hers, sometimes mumbling, sometimes whispering, and I felt my eyelids growing heavy in the dim glow of the oil lamp and from the heat of the fire, as my hands worked on those skins. I can't remember exactly when I heard her telling me about a red birthmark and utter the name 'Kate' in the middle of her story about Mary Carr's baby, but when she did, I sat bolt upright in my chair.

'Yes, the little girl was as perfect as can be, with a face like an angel. She had a cloud of dark hair and a red mark, crescent-shaped, like the moon, which ran the length of her thigh. Mary wanted to call her Polly, but she wasn't allowed. The child was taken by a couple who ran one of the tailor's shops over in the East End, who named her Kate.

'Mary thought that one day, that birth mark might help her be reunited with her daughter, but she'd made a promise never to seek her out, and she lived in fear of the asylum, so she kept her word.'

I stopped working and put down my rabbit skins.

'Something the matter, Alice?' said Pearlie, peering at me in the half-light. 'You look like you've seen a ghost.'

'I'm fine,' I lied. 'It's just the dust from these stupid rabbits. I need a drink of water.' I got up and walked to the sink to fill one of her chipped china cups. As I drank, I realised my hands were shaking. I thought back to the time Babyface had first stayed over at Mrs Dally's and I'd caught a glimpse of the red crescent-shaped birthmark on her leg as she got into bed beside me. Poor Babyface had no idea who her real mother was. It explained why she'd loved stealing so much, because it was in her blood. She was born to it, like a dancer or an artist, for that matter.

'But it doesn't end there!' said Pearlie. 'We ain't finished yet, see? So, you'd better sit back down and listen some more.'

I did as she asked because I wasn't sure I could stand for much longer. My chest was heavy, and I was gasping for breath, and not because of the fur-pulling. The guilt of what I'd done to Kate Felix, my Babyface, held me in a vice-like grip, almost crushing me.

'After the asylum superintendent took Mary Carr's baby and she was adopted by a tailor and his wife somewhere in the East End, Mary spent another fifteen years banged up in that asylum. Can you imagine that, Alice? Fifteen years of solitary confinement and punishments dreamt up by that wicked doctor. Oh, he did things to her that no woman should ever suffer. He had the keys to her cell, and after the adoption, he'd visit her whenever he fancied and force her to do things, unnatural things, saying if she didn't please him she'd be in a padded cell forever. The only thing that kept her going was her pal, the Whispering Girl, and the hope that if she didn't resist, she might be allowed to go back to sewing with the best-behaved inmates; his special girls, that's what he called them. They all suffered at his hands.'

She bowed her head and started muttering to herself, cursing under her breath, her fingers clasping a mother-of-pearl button, turning it over and over.

The question was burning on the tip of my tongue. I had to know the truth.

'Did you know Mary Carr in Bedlam, Pearlie?'

CHAPTER 25

MARY

Elephant and Castle, December 1925

I had grown old before my time, but the Whispering Girl was still as young as the day I was locked away in Bedlam and now she shrieked so loudly that I had to cover my ears to block out her howling.

'She'll betray you!' she cried. 'You can't trust her! I'm your only friend, Mary Carr! It's our secret and you've no right to tell her.'

Alice sat at the table a few feet away from me, her face etched with disbelief as I let out a low moan of agony. The years I'd spent trussed up in strait jackets, being plunged into icy baths, being punished just for wanting my brother and remembering my baby girl were my burden. My pain was in every stitch and every button of my pearly costume; in the disguise I'd created to hide my real identity from the world, for fear that I'd be found. And then, if I was discovered and they called me a child-stealer, I might not keep my temper and powerful people would come for me and lock me away forever.

The Whispering Girl warned me about the dangers constantly and I'd heeded her words and kept my promise to kind Dr Boothby, to never try to seek out my long-lost brother or my little girl. But when this young thief, Alice, crossed my path, I'd recognised something in her.

We were two sides of the same coin, minted in the Seven Dials, and it ignited something in me. I wanted to talk to her, to share my story. And once I started, I couldn't stop, even when the Whispering Girl was screaming at me.

'Be quiet!' I shouted at the voice yelling in my ear.

Alice's eyes went wide with surprise, and she reached down into her basket of fur-pulling and yanked out a bottle of brandy before uncorking it with her teeth and taking a large swig.

'Yes, I'm Mary Carr,' I said, as she took another drink. 'At least, I was a very long time ago. I was the Queen of Diamonds too, before they took everything from me. But they didn't manage to take this.'

I brandished my diamond ring. It had been safely tucked inside an old tobacco tin when Miss Comfort and her cronies took charge of all my worldly goods at the asylum and it was still there when I was released, during the Great War, in 1916.

'But that means you were Babyface's mother,' she said, her voice cracking with emotion.

I looked at her blankly. 'I ain't got the foggiest idea who you're talking about.'

'My friend, Babyface, who went to Holloway with me when we were caught because of her flaunting her fur coat,' she said, tears brimming in her eyes. 'Her name was Kate, she was raised by tailors in the East End because they told her that her real mother was dead. And she had the red birthmark on her leg. She was your daughter.'

I let her words sink in for a moment, watching her as she took another drink of brandy. I think she was expecting me to weep or grieve like a mother would. But my child had been dead to me for a very long time.

Instead, there was a space in my heart, filled with the shrieks and wails of the asylum and the endless whispers of my companion.

'The thing is, Alice,' I said, 'I'm very sorry that you lost your friend, Babyface – Kate, or whatever you want to call her. But I lost my child the moment she was born, and I never even knew her. The baby I had was called Polly. I only fed her once and saw her twice and every time I mentioned her, they hurt me for it. Do you understand?'

Alice started sobbing, properly crying, throwing her head down into her hands, her shoulders shaking.

'But I knew her!' she said, gulping for air. 'I knew her, and I let her down. She died because of me.'

'She died because she was in Holloway Prison,' I said flatly. 'And that was very bad luck, but she played a part in putting you both inside, as you well know. I read all about it in the papers.'

She grabbed for the bottle of brandy again, but I got out of my rocking chair and knocked it clean out of her hands. It smashed to pieces on the scullery floor and Geezer woke up with a yelp.

Then, I seized hold of her and shook her like a rag doll. 'I won't have you burying your problems in drink! I saw it with my own mother, and it ruined her. You've got to be stronger than that, Alice!'

'I can't!' she sobbed. 'I can't, there's nothing left of me to give.'

I tore the ring from my finger, holding it up to the light of the oil lamp.

'Look at it,' I said. 'See how it gleams and dances, with a life of its own. It's the perfect diamond, a real beauty, clear and pure. It will never age or let you down. Caring about people, loving someone, makes you weak. But the toughest and most beautiful diamonds are formed under pressure, Alice. You've either got to sparkle or be crushed.'

She gazed at it for a moment, and I took hold of her hand.

'What are you doing?' she said, trying to pull away from me. But I forced it onto her finger.

'It's yours but you'll have to earn the right to keep it,' I said. 'You're too clever and crafty for fur-pulling, it's a mugs' job. You need to find your spark, your grit, and get back out there with your girls, the Forty Thieves. A queen must lead. You just need to take the first step.'

She shook her head.

I tried again. 'You know how much I lost when I was Queen – my friends, my brother, my own child and my sanity. I was a mug because I cared too much, and I let my guard down. All I'm left with are the voices in my head and my flowers. But things can be different for you. I know they can.'

Geezer got out of his basket and came and sat beside her, gazing up at her and wagging his stumpy tail.

'It ain't that simple,' she said. 'There was somebody else, a fella who drove a wedge between me and Babyface, or maybe he found the weakness in her, and it all fell apart for us.'

I sighed. 'Well, if I had a pound for every useless bloke in London causing trouble between friends, I'd be a millionaire by now.'

She gazed into the fire, watching the flames dancing in the grate. 'It was like magic, how he took her from me. I got angry with Babyface because she fancied him, and I think I cared about her more than I've ever cared about anyone. But I discovered that too late. I behaved badly when she really needed me. I broke my promise to look

261

after her and she wasn't strong enough to make it on her own in Holloway. Now, it's like the fight has gone out of me.'

She slumped forward, her head in her hands, muttering, 'That bloke, Handsome, stole something from me.'

'You're a thief, ain't you?' I said, matter-of-factly. 'So, go and steal it back.'

CHAPTER 26

ALICE

Elephant and Castle, December 1925

My head was pounding when I was rudely awoken by Pearlie snatching the eiderdown from me and kicking me out of the bed in her scullery. I began to regret getting so well acquainted with the bottle of brandy the night before.

'Come on!' she said briskly. 'You've got work to do. I've let you sleep in! You can't be lazing about the place all day.'

I put my hands over my eyes and groaned, 'Oh, leave it out, Pearlie, just five minutes more.' I rolled over to face the wall, but Geezer jumped on top of me and started licking my face. That was revolting and I swear she made him do it, because when I sat up, she was laughing at me.

She'd already set out the teapot and a couple of hunks of day-old bread, with a smear of butter. My stomach felt queasy and I really didn't fancy a single bite of anything, but she wouldn't take no for an answer, so I relented and sat down, gingerly nibbling at the crust and slurping some tea.

'Hangovers are the devil's work, Alice,' she said. 'You'd better lay off the booze if you want to keep that ring.'

I looked at it, gleaming and perfect on my finger and felt a little flutter of excitement, like I did before the wheels came off and I ended up behind bars. She was right, but I was too exhausted by the truth of who she was, what she'd been through and what I'd done, to start any idle chitchat.

'So, what's your plan?' she said, as I picked at the last few crumbs on my plate. I'd already started to feel better, but I didn't want to give her the satisfaction of being right because I didn't want her to think for one moment that she was the boss of me. Give Pearlie an inch and she'd take a mile, I was sure of it.

If I was going to get even with Handsome, I'd need some new gladrags. It wasn't that there was anything wrong with my black velvet frock and fur coat, but he'd seen me wearing that before, and those fancy nightclubs only let you in if you were wearing the latest fashions. There was only one thing for it: I was going to have to go hoisting.

'Shopping,' I said, watching as she buttoned up her pearly jacket and plonked her hat on top of her head, tucking some strands of grey hair away from her face, which was lined and careworn. Now I understood why she looked so battered, after all that she'd been through. She broke into a smile at my news.

'Glad to hear it,' she said. She turned and put her hands on her hips, adding almost as an afterthought as she was heading for the door, 'I'll send Geezer with you to keep you company. If you want him to come to you at any point, just whistle like I do. He won't leave your side.'

'You're sending a dog out hoisting with me,' I scoffed. 'What's he going to do, use his paws to pinch some stockings?'

A look of anger crossed her face. 'Don't mock my dog,' she said. 'He's been more of a friend to me than anyone in this life and he's very clever and loyal. Plus, you're one of the only people I can think of he hasn't bitten, so he must like you.'

Geezer was sitting there gazing up at me with his long, egg-shaped face, his tongue lolling and his tail thumping ten to the dozen on the scullery floor. I tried to feel flattered by his attention, but it wasn't easy – he was quite an ugly-looking thing and his breath stank to high heaven.

'All right,' I said, throwing up my hands in defeat, 'He can come up to Gamages with me.' I patted him on the head. 'Welcome to my gang, Geezer.'

Geezer had a jaunty stride, bounding along on his powerful, muscular legs, his eyes glistening with mischief. You'd have thought he was proud to be out with me the way he strutted along as we went to deliver my piecework to the tallyman. But as we rounded the corner into the market, Geezer's pointed ears pricked up and he bared his teeth, making a low growl.

'Don't let that blooming hound anywhere near me!' said the tallyman, scarpering around the side of his cart for safety. 'The last time he jumped up and bit me, for no reason.'

I smirked to myself as I handed over my basket.

'Whatever did you do to upset him?'

'Nothing!' he replied. 'That dog is a bloody menace if you ask me. Here.'

He held out two shillings in his outstretched hand and I took them before he realised I'd only finished half the work. I turned on my heel and started to walk away, just as the tallyman shouted, 'Oi! Get back here!'

But Geezer turned and barked so loudly at him that he thought twice about chasing after us to ask for some of his money back.

'Well done, boy,' I said, patting him on the head. 'Seems like you might come in handy after all.'

We hopped on the next tram across the river, as the morning frost glinted on the cobbles. It was perishing cold, and I snuggled into my fur coat, grateful for the warmth of Geezer who sat at my feet as the tram rattled its way up to the West End.

The streets were thronged with people out Christmas shopping and taking in the window displays. I wandered around, starting in Oxford Street and working my way along to High Holborn. Of all the stores, Gamages was the most striking, with lights blazing in every one of its red-bricked arched windows, and paper decorations hung in great swags around huge model cars, train sets, dolls and bicycles for its Christmas Bazaar. Children had their noses pressed to the glass, looking longingly at gifts their parents could probably never afford. Further along the street, their mothers were gazing in wonder at floor-length sable coats, gorgeous dresses and dainty dancing shoes. In the middle of the window was the most stunning drop-waisted silk dress, adorned with shimmering bugle beads, which glinted under the electric lights.

I had my shoplifter's drawers on under my dress, and as I joined the crowds, I began to feel a familiar flutter of excitement. I'd made my mind up – I was going to find one of those fancy dresses and pinch it for myself. The joy of Gamages at Christmas was the jostling, bustling shopfloor, which provided the perfect cover for me, even without my girls to back me up. As I entered the store, I was dazzled by the colours and the number of people in there. My years in Holloway had been grey, drab and filled with boredom and grief, but this was another world, a world that I'd almost forgotten about. The queue for the tills snaked halfway around the department, and Christmas had brought out the best of the pile 'em high and sell 'em cheap mentality in the management, with heaps of silk stockings, leather gloves, spectacle cases, purses and wallets displayed under a huge sign which read 'Useful presents!'

I joined the fray, opening my carpet bag just under the table, sweeping a couple of packets of stockings inside it. It was easy and I felt a little glow of satisfaction. That's when I thought I caught a glimpse of a young woman who looked the spitting image of Babyface in the distance, over by the till. I looked again, rubbing my eyes in disbelief, but she'd gone. Still, I searched the crowd, willing myself to see her there smiling at me, just like she used to do. But I was alone, and my heart sank, my body flooding with that familiar, heavy feeling of guilt and grief. Just then, I felt something nudge my leg and it was Geezer, wagging his tail expectantly.

'Come on, then,' I said, as we pushed our way through to the make-up department. I leaned over the counter while the assistant's back was turned and swiped a lovely red lipstick as I passed by. It felt easy, like pinching a sweetie from the corner shop when I was a kid. We climbed the stairs, heading up to ladieswear, with Geezer taking two at a time. As I pushed through the double doors, I told him to sit.

'Wait there until I call you,' I said. He cocked his head on one side, as if he understood.

I glided across that floor, as if I was drawn by some unseen force, towards the most glamorous evening dresses, which took pride of place on a rail in the very centre of the room. Women were buzzing around those gowns like bees around a honey pot and I soon saw why. They shimmered as they were held up and admired, the delicate silk adorned with thousands of tiny bugle beads. There were murmurs of appreciation as details were pored over – a fringed hem, a drop waist, a panel of sheer silk, or embroidery with the finest silk thread. I elbowed my way forward, my fingers flicking through that rail, my heart pounding with excitement. My mouth went dry, and I began to shake as I felt the softness of the silk between my fingers. It wasn't the thrill of the hoist that had got me all flustered. All I could think of was Babyface twirling on that dance floor in the High Life, radiant, gleaming, shining like a star.

'Can I help you, Miss?' An assistant had joined the gaggle of women clustered around the rail. 'Might you like to try something? I could put it in the changing room for you.'

My reply stuck in my throat and I felt myself getting hot under the collar.

'Are you quite all right?'

'Just a bit warm,' I said. 'It's stifling, ain't it?'

She raised her eyebrows at me. My accent had given me away as a slum girl, not a wealthy young woman about town. It was a foolish mistake and one I'd never have made if Babyface were with me. There was no mistaking the sneer on her face. I didn't belong in here, with these expensive frocks. 'I'll take that dress, thank you,' she said, reaching out towards me, like a schoolmistress about to take something away from a naughty pupil. Other women were staring at me and whispering behind their hands. A working-class girl had invaded their little club, their wealthy world and their faces were a picture of scorn and amusement.

I bristled with indignation, glaring at them, feeling myself growing even hotter with a mixture of shame and anger, weighing up whether to hand over this beautiful dress, when Geezer scampered over and started to growl.

'Whose is this filthy dog?' screeched the assistant. 'No pets are allowed in here!'

Geezer didn't like that one bit and he showed that by nipping her on the leg. Not hard, but hard enough to make her yelp and move away. Someone else squealed, 'There's a mad dog on the loose!' and threw up her hands in horror, which only made him more excited. He ran around their legs, barking and nipping flesh wherever he could, as half a dozen well-to-do ladies started shrieking and leaping out of his way.

I locked eyes with the assistant.

'You ain't any better than me,' I snarled, snatching the dress from her grasp, and shoving it, still on the hanger, into my carpet bag. 'And my dog ain't filthy!'

It wasn't a pretty hoist, in fact it was a right mess and if it'd been one of my girls, I'd have torn a strip off her for it, but now I had the dress and I was running for the door while Geezer held everyone at bay, barking his head off.

At the last moment, I gave a loud whistle, and he came scampering after me just as Pearlie said he would, barrelling towards me at full pelt, knocking the displays flying. We both scarpered down the staircase in the confusion, and through the side exit, into the street.

Out on High Holborn, we melted into the crowds, and I gave him a little pat. 'Not bad for your first go at hoisting, Geezer.' Somewhere in the distance, I could have sworn I heard Babyface chuckling with delight.

The cars and buses were going at a snail's pace through the city, as the winter's afternoon drew in. I pulled the collar of my coat high around my neck to keep out the chill, hurrying through the backstreets towards Soho. I wasn't sure I could remember exactly how to find the High Life because there were so many seedy dives and jazz clubs in that part of town, and police raids for illegal drinking after hours meant many of them changed their names and their owners more often than I changed my underwear.

But as we rounded the corner into Brewer Street, stepping over piles of rubbish and rotten fruit in the gutter, I spied two dancing girls shivering outside a familiar doorway. They were dressed in silver shorts, with their stockings rolled daringly below their knees, held up by frilly garters. The poor cows had barely a picking on them, with their bony arms poking out of a feather boa slung around their shoulders, and on top of their heads, they wore a beaded headdress resplendent with white plumes. That was quite a feat because their necks were so scrawny they looked like they'd snap in a small breeze. Up close, you could see their pinched cheeks, flushed with rouge. Their teeth were chattering with the cold as they handed out bills to passersby, calling out, 'Masked ball tonight at the High Life!' and 'Pretty girls and prizes!'

I took a flyer, folding it into my pocket as Geezer looked up at me expectantly.

I started humming a tune I'd known as a girl. 'Half a pound of tuppenny rice, half a pound of treacle.

'That's the way the money goes.

'Pop goes the weasel.'

'Tonight, Geezer,' I said, matter-of-factly, as we headed back across the water, 'I'm going to be the belle of the ball.'

CHAPTER 27

ALICE

Elephant and Castle, December 1925

'That's a dress fit for a queen, that is!'

Pearlie clucked with delight like a proud mother hen as I held up my hoisted evening gown for her to admire, showing off the shimmering jet beads and the drape of the silk.

'Oh, you done good there, my girl,' she said, glowing with approval.

'I pinched it from Gamages,' I said with a little shrug. 'It wasn't so hard, not with Geezer there to help.'

'Told you he'd come in handy!' she replied.

He wagged his tail as Pearlie made a fuss of him.

There was only one fly in the ointment as far as my plan was concerned: I didn't have a mask for the party at the High Life later on.

'That's nothing to worry about,' said Pearlie, picking up her sewing box. 'I can make you one in a trice.' She pulled out a piece of felt and a scary-looking pair of shears and snipped two eye-holes in it, before opening her button box and tipping a pile of them onto the table. I watched in amazement as she threaded her needle and began to sew them on, in double quick time, until every inch was covered in shimmering mother-of-pearl buttons. Next she took two pieces of ribbon and stitched them into place so I could fasten it in a bow at the back of my head.

'I'm good at disguises, see?' she cackled, as I tried it on for size.

Next, I shrugged myself out of my velvet dress and pulled the silk gown up over my hips, wiggling a bit to get it over my bust. It fell to a flattering V at the front and the hem was fashionably fringed, swaying just below my knees. The dress shimmered in the light of the oil lamp as I walked towards the mantelpiece to peer at myself in Pearlie's tiny looking glass, which she had perched up there.

She gasped. 'Well, don't you look like you're headed for a night on the tiles!'

My hands were shaking a bit as I took the lid off the lipstick and started to outline my lips in the deepest shade of blood red. 'I ain't out to have fun, Pearlie,' I said, trying to not to smudge it, 'I've got work to do.'

She rifled through her sewing box and pulled out a cut-throat razor, with an ivory handle. 'In that case, you might be needing this,' she said.

The River Thames was an inky black ribbon, illuminated by a full yellow moon hanging low in the sky over London. I ignored the wolf whistles from fellas hanging on the street corners as I hurried on my way, my footsteps echoing on the cobbles. And there was another sound, of Geezer yapping as he chased after me, the silly hound. I tried to send him home, but he insisted on trailing a few paces behind me. The cloudless night was so chilly it made me catch my breath as I dashed up the steps to the bridge, to catch a tram across to the other side of the water, up to the West End.

It was only a few days before Christmas, and London was in a party mood, with pubs and bars overflowing. I even passed a line of office girls who were the worse for wear, doing the conga down Piccadilly. In Soho, a queue was forming outside the High Life, but I was in no mood for hanging around on the freezing pavement. I put on my mask, marched up to the doorman and opened my coat, my hand on my hip, giving him a glimpse of my shimmering beaded gown, which only a very wealthy young woman could afford. He tipped the corner of his hat at me and ushered me inside as a few girls behind me tutted in annoyance.

Music thrummed up the stairwell as I put my fur coat into the cloakroom and checked my lipstick in the mirror. Pushing through the doors into the nightclub, the air was already blue with smoke and the dance floor was rammed with couples shimmying and foxtrotting, in a mass of beads, furs and feathers. All the women wore masks – some were fringed and beaded, others were painted, like you'd see at a carnival, and their disguises made them more daring, hitching up their skirts and flashing their thighs as they danced.

The men were better-looking than I remembered, with their slicked back hair and their smart evening tailcoats. The whole room seemed to be pulsating with rhythm, moving in a blur, and the flashing, coloured lights of the dance floor made it harder for me to see clearly. I began to fear that I'd never spot him, not in this heaving crowd. But my pulse quickened as I glanced around the room, because there, dancing with a girl in a silver dress, was Handsome.

He was holding her in his arms, just as he had done with Babyface, cradling her like she was the most precious thing he'd ever laid eyes on. Time stood still and my stomach lurched. My mouth had gone so dry, I headed to the bar to get a drink and steady my nerves. I perched myself on a barstool, just as the band ended the song, and couples started to drift back to their tables. I was only on my own for a moment or two before some fella offered to buy me a drink, which was a relief because I wasn't sure I had enough money to afford more than one; the prices were ridiculous, to keep out the riff-raff.

He was a funny-looking bloke, with a pencil moustache, and talking to him was about as exciting as watching paint dry. He owned a motor car business up in Edgeware but was apparently looking for the love of his life.

'You could be that lucky girl,' he said, patting my knee. 'You shouldn't be out here all on your own in London town at Christmas. You need a good man to take care of you.'

I smiled through gritted teeth and took a sip of my drink, my diamond ring glinting under the glare of the electric lights.

He was just putting his hand inside his jacket to pay the barman, when someone else cut in. 'It's all right, old chum, I'm buying a bottle of champagne for my table, so I'll get this for the lady.'

I recognised his voice, and I looked back over my shoulder to see Handsome at my side, his eyes travelling appreciatively over my body. His gaze settled on the ring on my finger, and he broke into a dazzling grin.

My suitor, who was a full head shorter than Handsome, looked up at him and, realising he was hopelessly outclassed, muttered some excuse about going to find some smokes, retreating like a wounded animal.

I was gripping onto my cocktail glass so tightly that it was a wonder it didn't shatter. Blood was pumping through my veins. I hadn't yet worked out my plan to get even with him and just being beside him made me feel as if the floor was moving beneath me. I took a large gulp of my drink.

'Perhaps you'd better have another one?' he teased, shouting over the band which had started up again. 'You seem to have worked up quite a thirst.' His eyes searched my face. 'Have we met?'

I shook my head, grateful for my disguise.

'No, I'm sure I'd remember if we had,' I said, putting on the poshest accent I could muster when my heart was leaping into my mouth.

'That's a lovely diamond,' he said, pointing to the ring on my finger and gazing at it more closely. 'Handed down from your mother, I suppose?'

'It was a gift, from a distant relative,' I stammered. 'I'm an orphan.'

'Oh, bad luck,' he said, leaning in a bit closer. 'Me too. My father went down with the *Titanic* on the way to an art exhibition in America and my mother, well, she never really had any time for me, so after he died, I was packed off to boarding school and left in the care of the governess during the holidays. And then, poor dear Mama passed away not long after I inherited my father's title.' He brushed some imaginary dust from his jacket. 'So now I have no one to disapprove of me.' He smiled again and ran his hands through his hair.

Pearlie's cut-throat razor was safely tucked inside my brassiere, and I was sitting so close to him, it wouldn't have taken much to whip it out, flick it open and cut him a nice stripe on his perfectly smooth cheek. But I was frozen, mesmerised and horrified by him at the same time. His voice was hypnotic. He was the reason me and Babyface ended up in jail and he was close enough for me to scratch his eyes out.

'But I'm talking too much,' he said, 'I didn't catch your name?'

In that moment, I thought of Babyface and what her life might have been if she hadn't been separated from her real mother at birth and forced to work for strangers; if she'd never met me and never ever had the misfortune to lay eyes on him.

'Polly,' I replied drily.

'Won't you join me and my companion at our table, Polly? I'd hate to see you stranded over here at the bar with that dreadful chap all evening. He looked like the most terrible bore.' I nodded and stood up, following him back to the table, where the girl in silver was sporting the most gorgeous mask, encrusted with dazzling rubies. She was giggling as she watched other women dancing the Charleston, flinging their arms and legs about.

'Oh, there you are!' she cried, clapping her hands with glee. 'I was beginning to think you'd given me the cold shoulder.'

'Constance, meet my new friend, Polly,' said Handsome, setting the champagne bottle down on the silver tray in the middle of the table.

'Delighted to meet you,' she said, holding out her hand. Her wrists were adorned with rows of diamond and ruby bracelets. She looked like she'd raided a jeweller's shop. 'Are you having fun?'

Her hair was cut short, falling just to her ears, and she'd secured sections of it away from her face with diamond-studded hair clips, which glinted as they caught the light.

'I was expecting to meet someone, but he hasn't arrived yet,' I lied. 'So thank you for letting me join your little party.'

'Oh, such a shame, but his loss is our gain, so you're most welcome!' she said, letting out a shriek of delight as Handsome popped the champagne cork and it whizzed up towards the ceiling. 'Why don't we all dance?'

We knocked back a glass of champagne each and I felt the bubbles fizzing on my tongue, as the music grew louder. Before I knew what was happening, Handsome led us both out onto the crowded dance floor, where he took turns spinning us into him and away again, as we tried not to bump into other people. Constance was laughing so hard she almost tripped over and she was caught just in time by a man who'd taken off his tailcoat and loosened his bow tie. He was wearing a feather boa around his neck, and she clung to him as he pulled her away to dance the foxtrot.

Handsome seized his opportunity to pull me in close, his arm around my waist, his fingers touching the small of my back, making me giddy with desire, no matter how hard I fought that feeling. We were moving in time, perfectly in step with each other, as if we were born to be dance partners. He locked eyes with me.

'I bet you're very beautiful behind that mask, Polly,' he breathed in my ear.

I closed my eyes, picturing Babyface, pale and thin in her prison uniform, willing myself not to give in to his seduction. I was giddy from the champagne. My guts twisted inside me, and I began to feel sick.

'I think I need to sit this next one out,' I gasped, pulling away, and heading back to the table.

He followed me, with a look of concern etched on his features.

'Let me get you a drink of water,' he said, darting away to the bar. He returned with a glass and watched me take a sip.

'This calls for more champagne,' he said, with a laugh. 'I'm told it's a general cure for all kinds of ailments.' He sloshed some more into my empty glass and poured another for Constance. 'I'm sure she'll be thirsty too, if she ever returns,' he quipped, gazing towards the dance floor.

I glanced away, to fix my lipstick and ensure that my mask was still secure. As I turned back around, I caught a glimpse of him putting a little glass bottle back into his jacket pocket, just as Constance emerged from the crowd, flushed, and grinning like a fool.

'That was fun!' she screeched. She reached out to take the glass of champagne he offered her, just as the band leader stood up and announced the competition for the best mask of the evening. I pretended to take the teeniest sip of my drink, but Constance threw her head back and drank the lot in a couple of gulps.

'Shall we join the contest, Polly?' she said, seizing my hand and dragging me out of my seat. I could tell she wasn't going to take 'No' for an answer, so that's how I found myself lining up with all the debutantes and flapper girls, to whistles of appreciation, as the band belted out jazz.

There was a drum roll.

'And now, it's time to choose the belle of the Christmas ball,' the band leader intoned. 'Our generous sponsor, Lord Jeremy Harcourt, will pick the winner! Tonight's first prize is ten guineas!' There were whoops and shouts of approval from around the room.

I watched, dumbstruck, as Handsome got out of his seat, and made his way to the dance floor, grinning from ear to ear, and began to walk along the line-up to judge the contest. I felt my knees almost giving way as the penny dropped, and I realised why I recognised his name – he was Pearlie's little brother, the boy adopted by Lord and Lady Harcourt, which had broken her heart and made her lose her mind. He was the reason I'd turned my back on my best friend. He was the man I wanted to hurt, more than anything in this world, for what he'd done to me and Babyface. And now he was kissing me on the cheek, and presenting me with ten guineas as the winner of the masked belle of the ball.

'I've always had a liking for mother-of-pearl buttons,' he smiled, 'ever since I was a little boy. So, your mask wins first prize.'

My legs started to sway beneath me, but Constance went one better than that; I felt her slump against my shoulder, and then she fell forwards in a swoon. But the most amazing thing was, it was as if Handsome was expecting it, because he caught her, as gasps went up from everyone gathered around us.

'I think she's had a little too much to drink,' he said jovially, as I stood there, holding my prize money, my mouth falling open in shock.

'I'll help you take her home.' The words were out of my mouth before I'd even had time to think about what I was saying. We slung an arm each around our shoulders and helped her across the room, towards the stairwell, her head lolling to one side, her feet stumbling. We stopped at the cloakroom. He gathered her in his arms as I pulled on my coat, and we dragged her up the stairs while the doorman called us a cab.

'Montagu Square in Mayfair, please,' said Handsome, as he and the doorman manhandled Constance onto the back seat next to me. I looked at his face, as if I was seeing him for the first time, recognising something in his eyes which reminded me of Pearlie, his sister. He didn't look in the least bit concerned about Constance, who was mumbling incoherently; in fact, he looked quite pleased with himself. I began to wonder exactly what he'd put in her drink. I hadn't been imagining that, had I?

'Can I drop you off anywhere on the way?' he said, as if we'd just been out for a pleasant day trip and it was normal for us to be sharing a taxi home with a semi-conscious aristocrat.

'I can walk home from Mayfair, it's fine,' I replied, as the car set off, slowly making its way through the warren of backstreets, which were still choked with traffic as cabbies plied their trade. Above the noise of Soho, I heard a dog barking loudly, and glanced out of the back window, to see Geezer racing down the road after us.

'I don't expect her mother will be very pleased,' said Handsome, as we drew up outside a grand, tall mansion. 'You'd better wait here.'

I gazed up at the house. This was a place where the lords and ladies lived; people who never had to worry about paying their bills or putting food on the table. Then, I glanced down at my diamond ring, twinkling on my finger, thinking of how it belonged in one of these big houses, but had found a life on the streets; first with Pearlie and now with me, a slum girl daring to step outside her social class. That gave me determination to do what I needed to make things right.

The cabbie helped Constance down into Handsome's arms and then drove off. I lingered on the pavement, watching him walking her up the front steps, her head still nodding down towards her chest. She was mumbling something incoherent about not wanting any fuss. He rang the bell and a few moments later, the door was opened by a butler who looked aghast but clearly valued his job enough not to speak out of turn. Handsome accompanied Constance inside and the door swung shut.

In that instant, I made my move, darting a few paces along the street, to hide behind a post box. I pulled my cut-throat razor from my brassiere and opened it, gasping as I tested the sharpness of the blade on my thumb. I was crouching down, getting ready to spring out from my hiding place to get even with Handsome, when Geezer padded around the corner and came bounding over. He licked my face. He had followed us all the way from Soho, the crafty hound.

'Get off!' I whispered. 'You'll give me away, you silly fool.'

I swear he looked a bit hurt. He cocked his head on one side and went across to the railings surrounding the garden square to lift his leg. I watched the light going on in the bedroom at the front of the house, and then going out, before Handsome reappeared on the front steps, as the butler closed the door behind him. He glanced around the street, and then he called my name out into the dark, 'Polly! Polly!'

The moon slipped behind a cloud, and I hunkered low, listening for his approaching footsteps. But they didn't come. I peeked out from my hiding place and saw, to my utter astonishment, that he'd taken off his tailcoat and hung it on the railings. He was in his shirtsleeves now, climbing up the drainpipe, heading towards the first-floor window, where the light had been.

'What on earth are you playing at?' I muttered to myself, unfastening my mask and sticking it into my coat pocket. Across the street, Geezer whined and scampered to my side. I gave him a reassuring pat.

I watched in shock as Handsome reached across from the drainpipe and clambered onto the roof of the portico, before using all his strength to force the sash window up. Curtains billowed through the gap as he climbed inside but there was no scream. Constance must have passed out cold, aided by whatever he'd slipped into her drink. He was only in there a matter of minutes before he climbed out of the window again and pulled it shut behind him. He shinned back down that drainpipe as easily as one of the lads from around the Elephant up to no good and landed with a gentle thump on the pavement. He pulled something out of his pocket and stuffed it into his jacket, which he slipped back on. Then he started whistling to himself, heading down the street towards me.

'It's now or never, Geezer,' I whispered, waiting until the footsteps were right by the postbox. I sprang forward, using all my strength to catch him unawares, toppling him backwards against the railings, with the razor at his throat. Geezer, God love him, bounded at him and sank his teeth into Handsome's calf, making him yelp in agony.

'What in God's name are you doing, Polly?' he gasped.

'Be quiet!' I hissed. 'Or I swear I'll cut you from ear to ear.'

Geezer's jaw locked tighter around his leg.

A look of recognition crossed his face. 'Alice! Look, whatever this is about, can't we just discuss it without your dog biting my leg off?'

'Geezer's an English Bull Terrier, who doesn't let go that easily, once he's got his teeth into something,' I replied. 'A bit like me. The funny thing is, once their jaws lock, you can't get them off you. So, I've got a bone to pick with you, Jeremy.'

My face was just an inch from his own. I could see his Adam's apple bobbing against the cold, hard metal of my blade. I dipped my hand into his pocket and pulled out a ruby and diamond bracelet.

'I never had you down as a jewel thief. It ain't as if you need the money, is it? You're a lord!'

'If you let me go and call your dog off, I can explain,' he said. 'But it's hard to talk with a knife at my throat.'

'It's a razor. I ain't moving, so you'd better start talking before Geezer gets bored and takes a proper chunk out of you.'

I grabbed hold of his crown jewels to make my point, squeezing hard, bringing tears to his eyes. Geezer let out a low growl.

'All right! I'll talk,' he gasped. 'I've been stealing jewels to keep myself amused for some time. Surely as a thief you understand that?'

'I understand you grassed me and my pal up to the cozzers,' I replied, keeping a firm grip where it mattered.

'Only because it was turning up the heat on me, having you making such high-profile thefts. I needed to ensure the police felt I was beyond reproach. I'll say sorry if that'll make you feel better . . .'

'Selfish git,' I muttered. I can't deny it, I was enjoying bringing tears to his eyes.

'I told you my father went down with the *Titanic* and the tragedy claimed the life of my older sister too, who'd been accompanying him on that voyage. My mother had never been able to bear the sight of me but after they died, she made no effort to disguise her contempt. The only thing she really loved were her diamonds. I know it was wrong of me, but to spite her I used to steal things from her jewellery box and hide them. I took them, little by little, the things she loved, the diamonds she prized above me. She fired her maids, suspecting them of stealing from her and in the end, she even got rid of the housekeeper, who was loyal to a fault because she used to take great delight in making my life a misery, on behalf of my mother.'

'Lady Dorothy Harcourt,' I said.

Even in the gloom, I could see he'd gone as white as a sheet.

'How on earth do you know that?'

'I know a lot of things about you, Jeremy, such as where you live in Grosvenor Square, for instance.'

'In that case you know I'm wealthy, and we could work together and make a really good thieving team,' he ventured, his face softening. 'Just stop being silly. This acting all tough business doesn't suit you – it isn't very ladylike.'

I felt that stupid flutter of excitement in my stomach. But then I heard Pearlie's voice in my head, warning me that falling for someone, letting them in, was just weak.

'I ain't acting,' I said, pressing the blade a little harder against his throat. 'So, tell me the rest while you can still draw breath.'

'My mother fell sick with influenza. I'd never felt that I belonged, and it wasn't a surprise when I searched my father's desk and found some adoption papers. I confronted her about it, and even as she lay seriously ill, she taunted me that I was the child of a beggar woman and that my sister was a notorious thief. She died a few days later and I suppose I decided then to make a career for myself, stealing gems from wealthy girls, just for the hell of it.'

'Just for the hell of it?'

'My mother told me I was a guttersnipe, a ragamuffin, someone whose family lived by stealing. So, if you think about it, I'm just following a family tradition, of sorts.'

He laughed at his own pathetic joke.

'You took something from me which was worth more than diamonds when you grassed me and my friend up,' I said. 'I can never get that back.'

'Alice, you know I could get to care very deeply about you,' he said. 'We could have a great future together, but you've got to trust me and forgive what happened in the past, from one thief to another.' His voice was mellow, smooth and reassuring; only his widening pupils gave away his fear.

'You'll never understand what it is to be poor, to live your life worrying about where your next meal is coming from or whether the rent man might come calling!' I shot back. 'Thieving ain't a game for me, and it wasn't for my friend Babyface, either. It's a way of life. I want to give you a reminder of what happens when you stray onto my side of the tracks, Lord Harcourt, and play with the likes of us.'

Before he had time to think, I shifted the blade upwards towards his cheek and drew it down, slowly, just below his left eye, watching the blood ooze out of the gaping wound. He let out a low groan of agony and put his hand to his face, 'What have you done? You bitch!'

'I've settled a score for an old friend,' I said, feeling the thrill of seeing him bleed coursing through my veins. It was almost as good as stealing a beautiful fur. 'It's just a warning, Handsome,' I said, taking a step back, admiring my handiwork.

He let out a cry, fumbling for a handkerchief to stem the flow of crimson coursing down his face. 'You'll regret this!' he hissed.

'If our paths cross again, Your Lordship, you can bet I'll have the rest of my gang with me, and you will regret it very much. You're nothing but a poor little rich boy who wants to play at being a tea-leaf, ain't you? You left the Seven Dials when you could barely walk, so leave the stealing to those who really are born to it.'

My diamond ring glinted under the light of the street lamp and I made a silent promise to myself, never to let another man get the better of me and to be as hard as the stones I loved the best.

'Stay off our turf and keep your mouth shut, unless you want a matching stripe on the other cheek,' I said.

I whistled to Geezer as I turned to go, and he trotted dutifully to my side. I made my way home through the streets of London in the moonlight, knowing in my heart that when the sun rose, I would be Queen again.

EPILOGUE

ALICE

London January 1926

The Hoisters' Code

1. *A hoister never wears what she steals.*
2. *All hoisted goods are the property of the Queen of Thieves, to be sold on.*
3. *No hoister will try to pinch or flirt with the boyfriend of another hoister.*
4. *A hoister will never grass or help the cozzers.*
5. *A hoister will not booze or have late nights before shopping trips.*
6. *A hoister's wages will be paid weekly.*
7. *The Queen's decision is final.*

Now, don't get me wrong, I've always believed that rules are there to be broken, or at least bent a little bit, but I knew I needed to lay down a few laws of my own to make the Forty Thieves a successful gang.

A good Queen learns from their mistakes. I expect Good Queen Bess made a few errors in her time, but she mostly chopped other people's heads off for them. I don't have that liberty, although my razor does come in handy to show my displeasure. I prefer me and my girls to all be singing from the same hymn sheet, so we follow *The Hoisters' Code*; and these days, there's quite a bunch of us.

Bertha and Gert were over the moon when I came back to Queen's Buildings with blood on my hands and a twinkle in my eye after the night I got even with Handsome. It didn't take much for us to persuade the Partridge girls to rejoin us; they were bored rigid bottling jam. Ernie didn't say boo to a goose when I made off with a few more of his best workers too. And from there, we've gone from strength to strength, recruiting sisters, aunts and cousins all over South London. In any week I'll have three or four teams going shopping at least three times a week up in the big stores and some of the more enterprising girls have even taken to hopping on trains to other cities to carry on the good work.

I do look forward to the post on those days because the crafty minxes package up their most valuable goods and send them to me in the Royal Mail. It's so reliable. The only one who ain't so happy with this turn of events is the tallyman, whose face is as long as that nag of his every time our paths cross.

'Chin up!' I told him last time I laid eyes on him. 'They say there's going to be a General Strike, so I doubt people will be keeping up their repayments to you for much longer.'

I don't charge interest on my sales, and I am very reasonable about repayments because there are so many ways housewives can help me and the gang, whether that's storing some furs or tipping me the wink when the policeman's on his way round to my manor. And all this civil unrest and marching and rioting by the factory workers about pay keeps the cozzers busy, don't it? While the cat's away, the mice will play – up in Selfridges and Gamages, in my case.

The only sad thing was, not long after I took up my crown as Queen of Thieves, my old mate Pearlie, the flower seller, went to a better place. She was found on New Year's Day slumped on the bench in the garden overlooking number 7 Grosvenor Square. The street sweeper said she'd been selling lucky lavender door-to-door to the posh folk, who are more generous to people on the knock over the festive season. He thought she was asleep at first but when he reached out to shake her from her slumber, she was stone cold, with a mother-of-pearl button clasped in her frozen fingers.

She was peaceful, smiling even.

And the frost on the brim of her hat was sparkling, like diamonds.

Author note

Diamonds, the purest of all sparkling gems, are at the very heart of this novel, but the action unfolds through the eyes of one very rough diamond, Alice, in her quest to become the leader of a notorious gang of shoplifters, the Forty Thieves.

As the only writer on this subject to meet the relatives of the real-life Forty Thieves shoplifting gang, I was always determined to write a whole series of books about their exploits, to bring to life the unique insights I gained into their secrets.

And it may seem a little strange to write the beginning of the series, covering the turn of the 19th century and into the roaring 1920s at the end of that process, but for me, it all makes perfect sense.

The Alice I learned about first-hand was a fully-fledged *Queen of Thieves*, ruling her roost in the 1940s. To those who knew the real Alice Diamond, who went by a number of aliases – Dolly Black, Alice Blake, Norah Emerald - her past was always a bit of a mystery. But her influence on a generation of working-class women who had few prospects is undisputable. Even today, speaking to people who grew up around the Elephant and Castle who had relatives who knew the Forty Thieves in the years before the Second World War, her name still evokes responses which range from pride and nostalgia, to disapproval and anger at the gang's shocking criminal behaviour.

The more I have written about my fictional character Alice Diamond in the **Queen** series, the louder her voice has echoed inside my head. I have been compelled to dig deeper into her origins, to find what traces I could about this remarkable woman. I dug them up from historical sources including court records, newspapers and secret police files. I suppose I wanted to try to piece together her motivation for being not only a shameless thief, but a woman living the high life on the wrong side of the law when the norm was to work in a factory or stay at home like a good housewife.

Her cool demeanour when arrested and her sheer cheek in the face of authority leaped off the page at me, when she calmly told the judge that the theft of a fur coat worth thousands, was 'Nothing to do with me, your Honour' - even though she'd been caught wearing it around town with the shop label still inside it.

Newspaper cuttings from her arrests for larceny in the 1920s suggest that she was married young, but no records of that have been found. She is also said to have had children - using this fact to plead for leniency in court. Yet the children who could have been hers appear in official records as her mother's. Perhaps it is just another case of Alice bending the facts to suit her needs when she was collared by the law...

Jewels were an easy target for Alice and her girls because they were small, with a high value, but easy to hide about their person; under their hats, up their sleeves or slipped into special secret pockets sewed inside their coats. Sometimes temptation got the better of the gang in the 1920s, and they'd daringly - or foolishly - snatch entire trays of rings and make their get away through Soho, with the police and shopkeepers in hot pursuit.

It was all a world away from the drudgery of factory jobs in South London, which were the reality for most young women her age. So, it wasn't long before Alice had gathered a gang of like-minded girls who became very skilled at hoisting from shops all over town.

After dark, she loved putting on the posh, dressing up in fine silk dresses, to go dancing in illicit drinking dens and nightclubs in Soho. Legend has it that she once took first prize in a foxtrot competition against other Flapper Girls. Her gang were the best-looking thieves in the Café de Paris and latterly, Holloway Prison.

But Alice and the Forty Thieves did not just spring out of nowhere in the 1920s and that's where the story got really interesting. I discovered that she was undoubtedly inspired by the first Queen of Thieves, a daring girl from the London slums of the 1880s, called Mary Carr.

Mary was born poor but was incredibly beautiful, with a grace that made it easy for her to pass herself off as a wealthy young woman when she went stealing in the posh shops up in Oxford Street at the turn of the century.

She was an artist's model, known as the 'Swan-necked Beauty' and even posed for drawings and paintings by a female aristocrat, who enjoyed touring the slums in search of what she called, 'happy poverty'.

The very idea of a wealthy woman portraying abject poverty in a positive light was so repugnant to me that the character of Lady Dorothy was born. And it is true that her models were sometimes asked to dress up in rags if their own clothes weren't dirty or patched enough.

Mary Carr was portrayed as a young flower seller, a girl playing with urchins and a young mother cradling a sleeping child. One can only imagine what Mary made of this, but its fair to say that when she appeared in court on the shocking charges of stealing a child, perhaps to force payment from his parents as part of a criminal enterprise, she was resplendent not in rags, but in a velvet cape, diamonds and a hat adorned with ostrich feathers.

Her commanding presence drew gasps from the packed public gallery as she protested her innocence.

She may have been an urchin and a flower seller, but Mary Carr was a Queen at heart.

I hope you have enjoyed reading the other books in the series, **Queen of Thieves** and **Queen of Clubs**. The story of the Forty Thieves runs through generations of London women who found a way to take what wasn't rightfully theirs in the hope of lifting themselves out of the gutter. Their greatest prize was sparkling diamond rings, which in true Forty Thieves style, Alice also used as a knuckleduster, combining the dazzle of the jewel with the potential for violence. So, Alice became the **Queen of Diamonds** as she learned her dubious craft of hoisting, which always involved the fight to keep her crown as leader.

It speaks volumes that her criminal antics continue to fascinate today.

So, perhaps diamonds really are forever.

Acknowledgements

Writing a book can be a lonely experience at times and that's why having a wonderful literary agent and publisher is so crucial for writers to flourish.

I am really lucky on both counts, with Laura Macdougall of United Agents and Rhea Kurien of Orion, who both understand my writing so well and are such a great support.

Thanks also to Laura's assistant Olivia Davies at United for always being there and also Orion's team, Sanah Ahmed, Sahil Javed and Clare Wallis, for her attention to detail.

A special mention goes to Hannah K, who shared my enthusiasm for the research into Victorian and Edwardian London on some fabulous days out around the big city, looking into the life of the first *Queen of Thieves*, Mary Carr.

Reuben, you rock my world, and I'm always grateful to my friends Sally, Lisa, Jules and all my readers who have followed the adventures of the Forty Thieves with me and encouraged me to keep writing about them. Beverley Ann Hopper, Marc Alan Powers Egan, and Julie Boon, your encouragement means so much to authors.

I began to write books more than a decade ago so that I could spend time at home with my sons while they were growing up. So, this one is for you boys, and don't forget to empty the dishwasher.

London, 1946.

Alice Diamond, the Queen of the Forty Thieves, rules over her gang of hoisters with a bejewelled fist. Nell is a slum girl from Waterloo, hiding a secret pregnancy and facing a desperately uncertain future.

Sensing an opportunity to exploit Nell's vulnerabilities, Alice takes her under her wing and, before long, Nell is experiencing the secret world of hoisting, with all the dangers - and glamorous trappings - that comes with this underworld existence.

Alice has a longstanding feud with Billy Sullivan's all-male gang in Soho, and thinks Nell could be a useful weapon in her vendetta. But Nell has a secret agenda of her own, and is not to be underestimated. And the more she is exploited by both Alice and Billy, the more her hunger for revenge grows. As she embraces the seedy underbelly of London, will she prevail in carving out her own path to power and riches...

...and crown herself the Queen of Thieves?

1957, London.

Gangland Queen Nell has the perfect life of crime as a top shoplifter by day and glamorous club owner by night. But a betrayal and botched robbery suddenly reverse her fortunes... and her old rival, Alice Diamond, is hell-bent on taking her down.

After escaping a poverty-stricken childhood, nightclub dancer Zoe has more on her mind than settling scores for Alice. But the life of luxury Zoe craves comes at a terrible price. And when a vicious gang tightens its grip on Soho, all three women realise it pays to keep your friends close and your enemies closer.

When the fight to save your family becomes a fight for survival, there is no honour among thieves...